Penguin Books
The Slumbering Sentinels

Born in Colombo, Sri Lanka, in 1926, Christopher Gregory
Weeramantry has had unusually varied opportunities to
observe the law in differing settings – forensic, judicial and
academic. Brought up in a legal system combining English,
Roman Dutch and Customary law, he practised for
seventeen years at the Bar in Sri Lanka before his
appointment to the Supreme Court as its youngest Judge
ever. He served on the Bench for seven years, observing at
close quarters the interrelationship between political power,
law and the judiciary in a rapidly changing society.

C. G. Weeramantry is a Doctor of Laws of the University
of London and has since 1972 been Professor of Law at
Monash University, Melbourne. Among his books are:
A *Treatise on the Law of Contracts* (2 vols), 1965; *The Law in
Crisis*, 1975; *Equality and Freedom: Some Third World
Perspectives*, 1976; *Apartheid: The Closing Phases?*, 1980;
and *An Invitation to the Law*, 1982.

He has long been interested in the impact of technology
on legal and human rights protection and has addressed
numerous seminars and conferences on this topic, both in
Australia and overseas.

Professor Weeramantry is married, with five children,
and lives in Melbourne.

C. G. Weeramantry

The Slumbering Sentinels
Law and human rights in the wake of technology

Penguin Books

Penguin Books Australia Ltd,
487 Maroondah Highway, P.O. Box 257
Ringwood, Victoria, 3134, Australia
Penguin Books Ltd,
Harmondsworth, Middlesex, England
Penguin Books,
40 West 23rd Street, New York, N.Y. 10010, U.S.A.
Penguin Books Canada Ltd,
2801 John Street, Markham, Ontario, Canada
Penguin Books (N.Z.) Ltd,
182-190 Wairau Road, Auckland 10, New Zealand

First published by Penguin Books Australia, 1983

Typeset in Goudy Old Style by Dovatype, Melbourne

Made and printed in Australia by
Dominion Press Hedges & Bell

CIP

Weeramantry, C. G. (Christopher Gregory), 1926-.
The slumbering sentinels.

Bibliography.
Includes index.
ISBN 0 14 022498 X

1. Civil rights - Australia. 2. Technological
innovations - Law and legislation - Australia
I. Title.

342.94'085

Contents

Foreword

The Hon Mr Justice M. D. Kirby, CMG
Chairman of the Australian Law Reform Commission

In an earlier Penguin Book, *Science and Human Values*, that great science communicator, the late Professor Jacob Bronowski, wrote in 1975:

To think of science as a set of special tricks, to see the scientists as the manipulators of outlandish skills – this is the root of the poison mandrake which flourishes rank in the comic strips. There is no more threatening and no more degrading doctrine than the fancy that somehow we may shelve the responsibility for making the decisions of our society by passing them to a few scientists armoured with a special magic.

This book is about a new jurisprudence and a new sociology for the world of science and technology. Professor Weeramantry, a man who has practised, administered, judged and taught the law, brings a message which is specially relevant for our time. Like Bronowski, Weeramantry has made a crusade of communicating across barriers of professional specialization. In writing this book he has been particularly concerned that scientists and lawyers understand the problems each poses for the other, and also that the layman understands how these issues could affect our lives.

Three remarkable technologies have flourished in the past decade or so. They pose acute dilemmas for our society. Some of these are illustrated in this book:

• The new *energy sciences* present specially dangerous problems. The chief dangers arise out of the development of nuclear fusion. Professor Weeramantry cites an opinion suggesting that there is a 5 to 10 per cent chance of a serious nuclear accident before the end of the century. Thermal energy has dangers for the eco system. Petroleum involves the risks of serious oil spills and pollution. The world's rain forests are being destroyed to produce wood, some of it used for energy. The possibility of criminalizing 'ecocide' is raised in these pages.

● The new *information technology* is perhaps the most pervasive of the technological developments of our time. The impact of computers linked by telecommunications for privacy and for evidence law have already been mentioned. Numerous other information technologies are examined in this book for their impact on human values in and the vulnerability of modern society.

● But the problems of *biotechnology* are perhaps the most puzzling, precisely because they touch the most basic human facts of life and death. The dilemmas of transplantation have been studied. The quandaries of in vitro fertilization (test tube babies) are now under consideration by no less than five enquiries in Australia alone. But who is examining the problems of human cloning, DNA experimentation, mind manipulation, surrogate parenthood, community testing of new drugs, 'farming' of foetal tissue, and the many other bioethical riddles outlined in this book?

These projects illustrate, and Professor Weeramantry's book elaborates, the way in which law and society is adapting to scientific and technological change. Unhappily, it must be confessed that the number of the problems being presented, and the urgency which attends their resolution, far outstrip the present capacity of our lawmakers, and those who advise them to respond.

It is hopeful that among the 'slumbering sentinels' there is at least one which remains alert. Scattered through these pages are various references to the relevant work of the Australian Law Reform Commission. In almost every task given to that commission by successive Australian governments since 1975, the implication of science and technology and its laws have had to be tackled:

● In an early report on criminal investigation, the Law Reform Commission proposed the use of sound and video recordings to set at rest disputes about confessions to police. The use of photography for identification parades and the provision of arrest and search warrants by telephone were other features of a report seeking to adapt the law on police procedures to available modern technology.

• In a report on breathalyzer laws, proposals were made for the use of modern breath analysis equipment and other scientific means to detect intoxication, including by drugs other than alcohol.

• In a report on human tissue transplantation, the commission had to address the definition of 'death' for legal purposes and the many other bioethical questions posed by surgical transplant procedures, some of them reviewed in this book.

• In a report on defamation law reform, it was necessary to suggest adaptation of Australia's defamation laws to cope with the new technology of radio and television, telefacsimile and the rapid distribution of print media, all of which argue for a new, national approach to defamation law reform.

• In a report on the sentencing of federal offenders, it was necessary to examine the use of computerized statistics on sentencing, in order to secure greater uniformity in the judicial punishment of offenders.

• The current project on privacy protection requires examination of the impact on individual privacy of the growing computerization of personal information. The advent of optical and listening devices and techniques of telephonic interception all endanger individual privacy. They, too, are under consideration.

• The current work of the commission on evidence law reform requires examination of the modifications of the laws of evidence, necessary to adapt our trial system, long infatuated with oral evidence, to a world in which vital decisions will increasingly be made based on computerized data.

• Even a project on Admiralty jurisdiction, seemingly remote from the world of science and technology, requires the Australian Law Reform Commission to reconsider Admiralty law to ensure that new 'ships' such as hovercraft are embraced within it.

While law reform organizations in several parts of the technologically advanced world are besieged by a vast range of problems such as these, no one can doubt the importance of developing further and broader effective social responses to the new technology.

Not content with cataloguing the problems, Professor

Weeramantry lists a programme for action to repair the inadequacies of our social response to science and technology and to assure the survival of the rule of law in the age of science. Suggestions include the establishment of a science court and a science commission. Whether these or other institutional solutions are appropriate is only one of the questions posed by this book. It is timely to remind ourselves again of Jacob Bronowski's warning: 'The world today is made, it is powered by science; and for any man to abdicate an interest in science is to walk with open eyes towards slavery.'

This book seeks to open the eyes of a generation, so dazzled by technological innovations, that it is often blinded to the social and human dangers that need to be seen.

Preface

The preamble to the Universal Declaration of Human Rights reads: 'Recognition of the inherent dignity and of the equal and inalienable rights of all members of the human family is the foundation of freedom, justice and peace in the world.'

These values have been threatened before. In the name of an all-powerful state, a compelling religious belief or national aspiration, the 'interests of the masses', 'progress', or the unabashed pursuit of power, human dignity and equality have often been trodden underfoot and people converted into objects of ownership or manipulation. Under such overt attacks, legal protections, such as they were, have crumbled overtly.

Today the attacks are more subtle. Paradoxically, the process is defended in the name of freedom and the threat comes from one of mankind's greatest benefactors. Science and technology have burgeoned in the post-war years into instruments of power, control and manipulation. But the legal means of controlling them have not kept pace. Outmoded and outmanoeuvred by the headlong progress of technology, the legal principles that should control it are unresponsive and irrelevant. Legal structures and concepts and people who work the system are proving unequal to the task of protection, in the midst of a set of problems without precedent in the law. Assumptions long regarded as fundamental no longer hold true. Values once held unquestionable no longer command acceptance. Procedures once adequate no longer yield results. Lawyers are out of their depths, their concepts out of touch, their techniques ineffectual.

Sociologists, philosophers, economists, environmentalists, ecologists and politicians have sensed some of these dangers and prepared for them. Lawyers have been slow to do so, hampered by outdated concepts and methods.

The United Nations has for some years been conscious of this danger to human rights. On 10 November 1975, the General Assembly called on all states to prevent the use of scientific and technological developments to limit or inter-fere with human rights and basic freedoms.

I want to show how basic assumptions of the preamble to the Universal Declaration – inherent human dignity, equal and inalienable rights, universality, freedom, justice, peace – are threatened by powerful technologies functioning largely free of checks and balances. The disciplines of law and human rights (for human rights is now a discipline of its own) have slumbered when they should have been alert. The slumbering sentinels cannot much longer afford to sleep upon their watch.

Chapter 1

Science, Law and the Citizen

In July 1978, fifty law suits were filed against a San Francisco sperm bank for allowing its sperm deposits to thaw. Men who had had vasectomies or who feared that they might become sterile and had banked their sperm claimed that their sperm was spoiled when a container with liquid nitrogen tipped over it. Some of the claims ran to more than a million dollars and foreshadowed many legal and human rights issues. The technology of freeze-preserving sperm, evolved to meet the requests of soldiers going to the Vietnam battlefront, thus spawned a brood of legal conundrums from questions of posthumous paternity, limitations on the right to procreate, community control over artificial impregnation, and standards for selection of donees, to community duties towards the unborn child, foetal rights, privacy, abortion, maintenance and succession. Does the human right to procreate involve the right to procreate after one's natural death? If it does, for how many years or generations? What rights does the donee mother have against the estate of the donor? What rights of succession does a child have to a father who has been dead fifty years? What effect does its belated arrival have on children who have already succeeded to shares of the estate and have since disposed of them? When severe population pressures impose limits on the right of even the living to beget children, what claim have the dead to this luxury? Is it contrary to public policy to offer financial rewards generation after generation to women who will carry a dead millionaire's child? Is the storage of semen a simple matter of private contract between the donor and the sperm bank? What claims does the child have for defects caused through the artificial processes involved? And against whom?

In 1973, B. F. Goodrich announced the deaths of three poly-
vinyl chloride workers from cancer of the liver. Was the
danger caused by high concentrations of this chemical in the
plastics industry known earlier and were these deaths
preventible? The Manufacturing Chemists Association
(MCA) in the United States was aware of findings of the Italian researcher, Dr Cesare Maltoni, that vinyl chloride concentrations as low as 250 parts per million (half the allowed
exposure level for US workers) caused cancers in animals.
Despite a visit by its members to Dr Maltoni, the MCA did
not give this information to the National Institute of Occupational Safety and Health (NIOSH); it did not warn the
public; and it did not tell NIOSH, when it asked, about the
toxic effects of vinyl chloride.

Why? The data were withheld by agreement with the
European manufacturers. When the Maltoni data were
revealed, NIOSH lowered permissible exposure to one tenth
of the previous level.

Proprietary interests, private contracts, gentlemen's agreements and scientific secrecy had stood between the three
dead workers and their right to life and safe conditions of
work. Their deaths also raised other issues: the interlocking
of science and industry, the lack of social concern among
scientists, the need for a scientific ethic, the need for pre-
cautionary mechanisms by which scientists can draw attention to the dangers of their employers' projects without
threat to their jobs, the inability of courts to assess technological data, the inadequacies of regulatory agencies, the
dependence of courts on other agencies for fixing the level
of permissible hazards, and the possibility of deliberately
covering up scientific information for private profit.

All the fun of the fair was there at Aldershot – gay marquees,
loudspeakers, hawkers, hotdogs, free drinks. Most countries
had sent representatives, for all the 'free world' goes to
Aldershot to Britain's annual arms exhibition. The best of
British brainpower had gone into creating the exhibits, and
the results were on show.

A journalist asked a salesman how he compared his new
AR-18 5.56 millimetre gun with the Russian Kalashnikov.

'This leaves the Kalashnikov for dead', was the rather peeved reply. 'It has a much flatter trajectory. All you've got to do is to aim at his guts and fire. Up to 400 metres, you're sure to hit him somewhere between the head and the groin.' [1]

This trade in death is perfectly legal, sanctioned by national and international law. Indeed, the industry is an economic necessity: 10,000 British firms are involved in it and its revenue of nearly a thousand million dollars is crucial to Britain's economy. The best of British brain power has gone into creating the exhibits, in keeping with the fact that half the world's scientific endeavour devotes itself to the fabrication of weapons. [2]

The integrity of the human personality was far from the minds of those organizing this scientific, industrial and military circus. More significantly, this carnival of death went on without protest from a legal profession long accustomed to devoting its energies and talent to combating minor abuses of human dignity.

In the South Australian town of Port Pirie, a disused dam was a favourite place of play for schoolchildren. In it had been dumped 25 hectares of tailings, effluent from a government-sponsored uranium mill. Although levels at the dam exceeded World Health Organization (WHO) maximum standards, official reassurances had meant that no medical follow-up programme was undertaken.

These are some of the legal questions it raises: Is the health authority liable if negligence is proved? Who is responsible for the medical expenses of, and compensation for, contamination injuries? How is disability legally proved to have resulted from exposure years earlier to radiation pollutants? Will the children of the next generation be able to claim for defects resulting from genetic damage to their parents? Who compensates owners for loss of property value? What recourse do citizens have if the company responsible for damage is no longer in operation? Do courts and lawyers have the scientific expertise to deal with the questions of technical complexity that may arise? Is the adversary system of legal procedure suitable for the scientific fact finding necessary for establishing a legal case? And how does the citizen fight a legal battle on equal terms with the wielders of the technology, where massive commercial interests are involved under heavy government protection?

Before she developed breast cancer, Darleen Biggs used to sit for hours with a book in a cosy corner of her living room in her house in Salt Lake City. This favourite place was the hot spot of the house, which had been built on a foundation of tailings from the local uranium mill. Up to 200,000 tonnes of the tailings were embedded in the streets, drives, houses, offices and swimming pools of the city. But it required the Biggs case to move the health department into action.

In Grand Junction, where there were also tailings in the buildings, the rate of leukaemia among people over sixty-five was found to be twice the national average. The nature of the relationship between the tailings and particular cancers is not clear, but that there is some relation has meant that there is now the problem of disposing of twenty-five million tonnes of tailings dumped at more than twenty sites in eight states. By 1978, eleven states had banned nuclear rubbish dumps within their borders and many more were considering a similar ban. If all the states of the US make a similar decision, where will the hot rubbish be dumped? Could Washington impose dumps on unwilling state governments? To what extent can a federal government use 'national good' as a justification for taking risks that affect only local communities?[3] This is a problem in any federated nation. If the federal government has such powers, it is a cheerless situation for the citizens of a state; if it has not, a state may go its own selfish way and put the entire nation at risk.

In 1982, a paediatrician in the Coffs Harbour area in New South Wales reported a spate of babies born with congenital abnormalities, and called for a Department of Health inquiry. In the big banana plantations of the area, a pregnant woman exposed to crop duster sprays underwent three ultrasound scans as a precaution. According to a report in the *Age* newspaper in Melbourne in November 1982, she said, 'It turned out that the guy who took the scans thought the baby's head was in shadow; in actual fact the baby had no top on her head at all.' The child was born dead in 1981 with no brain and spina bifida. Her second child was born dead in 1982 with other gross deformities. The couple had had a healthy child before and had no history of abnormalities in their families.

Stephen, born in 1978, was a seriously deformed child whose home was near the sea. There were no suspect drugs, such as thalidomide, taken by Stephen's mother, and it may be that his condition was an accident of nature. But it was also known that Stephen's father regularly brought home fresh sea fish. Early in 1977 there had been an oil spill off the shore, and dispersants had been used to clear it up. What happens when oil combines with other pollutants in the water is largely unknown. Recent scientific research suggests the possibility that these millions of dispersed droplets of oil collect hydrocarbons, which induce cancers and mutations. These chemicals could affect humans by working along the food chain beginning with filter-feeding marine animals. Stephen's parents believe this was probably the cause of Stephen's condition. All the lawyers they consulted said categorically, however, that even if this were the case, legal proof would be impossible.

This situation could arise in any coastal area near an oil spillage dealt with in this manner. Throughout the world, hundreds of major oil spills from tanker accidents occur every year,[3] spilling thousands of millions of litres into the sea. The law is not equipped to prevent such dangers or to deal with them after they occur.

In Britain, Peter Smith spends a good part of each year giving information about himself to one or other of over 200 central government institutions.[4] Data banks in departments of motor registration, education, census, post office, land registry, inland revenue, customs and excise, employment, health and social security, police, probation, planning and housing now contain information on him. Further information is recorded in many private organizations, banks and credit agencies, and his technical school or university, insurance companies, employers' offices, doctors' surgeries, and travel agencies. The information could be assembled into a complete dossier on him. The flow of information from one data bank to another often takes place without his knowledge. The national police computer, for example, feeds information automatically into customs and excise, and motor registration into inland revenue and police. There is a direct information link between banks and credit agencies and customs and excise, social security and inland revenue, employment, hospital records and health insurance.

Such information networks cover a large section of the population. Millions of citizens have been convicted of some offence in a court of law; millions use credit agencies and bank cards; most of the population is registered for health purposes. Furthermore, the preparation of data tapes often takes place abroad, where national privacy laws do not extend.

There is little that people can do to protect their privacy for, very often, they are not even aware of the extent of information available to the authorities. British driving licences, in deference to the wishes of citizens objecting to the recording of dates of birth and sex, appear to omit this information but actually contain it in a thinly disguised code. The digits 309108, for example, contain the holder's date of birth – 10.9.38 – in jumbled form. Sex is indicated by adding 5 to the second digit for women. Other data indicated in the next set of digits are said to distinguish the holder from any other person with the same name born on the same day and could provide the framework for a national identity card containing racial, political and criminal identifiers. Under the guise of the humble driving licence or health registration card, the computer can impose '1984' surveillance on an unsuspecting public.[5]

In July 1981, the Australian Minister for Health called for an urgent report on a new product called humatrol, prepared from human blood and tissue extracts, and made and sold by the Commonwealth Serum Laboratories. The report was called for as a result of staff in a Melbourne laboratory seeking clarification of the legal and moral issues involved. The large-scale manufacture of humatrol would require, according to some estimates, tonnes of blood and kilograms of selected human tissues each year.[6]

Sale of human tissue is not new. Suppliers catering for the needs of medical laboratories have long been plying this trade, offering in their catalogues wide varieties of human tissue. The sources of supply are not necessarily announced.

Experimentation on the human body continues in hundreds of scientific laboratories, many of which follow strict ethical guidelines, but many of which do not.

Passengers using one of the US's busiest airports – Denver, Colorado – on 12 August 1981 could scarcely have realized that they came so near to 10,200 kilograms of nerve gas so powerful that two drops could kill. A massive airlift of this lethal substance was underway during a nationwide air traffic controllers' strike and on an aircraft the malfunctioning oil pressure gauge of which delayed take-off for fifty-three minutes.[7]

Governments have a duty to protect their citizens, and dangerous research near densely populated cities flouts this duty. Congress, facing up to this danger, belatedly ordered the Pentagon to destroy or move 888 'weteye' bombs because they were near Denver, and containers with material drained from leaking bombs were also moved.

International law has as yet been unable to outlaw scientific research aimed at perfecting means for the agonizing destruction of the human body. A small neutron bomb exploded 200 metres above ground produces neutron radiation exceeding 16,000 rads, causing an agonizing death lasting up to two days, for people within an area of 1.5 square kilometres. For those within the next square kilometre, the agony would last from two to six days, and for those further out, for up to thirty days. Nevertheless, research continues without protest from the legal systems within which they occur.

John, clever and ambitious, has risen rapidly in the public service to be deputy director of his department. This department is the public's watchdog in the field of the road transport industry, monitoring standards, issuing licences, receiving confidential information about every aspect of the services offered by dozens of operating companies. All this information is available to the senior people in the department, some essential features being carried in their minds but most details being stored in their data banks.

One of the largest operators in the field offers John a job as its manager on twice his present salary. John accepts. No law in most industrialized countries prevents this or delays the translation of public official into private operator. John's mind carries many secrets. If he is honourable – and super-human – he will try to divide his mind into two segments, imposing a barrier on the transmission of sensitive data from the official to the unofficial segment. If he is not, sensitive official data will become the property of the private sector. Computer technology has magnified this problem.

A team of atmospheric physicists at Goddard Space Flight Centre Laboratories reported in August 1981 that the earth's average temperature rose 0.2 degrees Celsius from the mid 1960s to 1980. It provided dramatic evidence that the earth was warming up at an alarming meteorological rate. The possible causes are a 15 to 25 per cent rise in carbon dioxide and other trace gases in the atmosphere from living fossil fuels, tonnes of lead being discharged monthly into the atmosphere, plastics manufacturing, motor emission fumes, aerosol sprays and a resulting gaseous blanket around the earth, trapping reflected heat in the famous 'greenhouse effect'. The possible effects are dramatic temperature increases by the end of the century, climatic change, melting of the polar icecaps, and corn belts transformed into dust bowls. The legal problems are how to make national and international environmental laws and controls effective, how to curb corporate power, how to conserve human rights to life, health, and a fair environment, and how to conserve the rights of posterity. If, as the Club of Rome once predicted,[8] earth's life support systems could collapse with awesome suddenness, the ineffectiveness of the law to control technology will have been one of the principal causes.

The examples used so far are already with us. Scenarios for the year 1999 will illustrate the kinds of legal conundrums with which scientific development could confront us.

In 1999, Phil's three mothers all waited anxiously as their seven-year-old son underwent surgery on his heart, which had been defective from birth. Elizabeth and Martha were his natural mothers: an egg from Elizabeth's ovary was fertilized in the laboratory with sperm from a sperm bank and carried to maturity in Martha's. uterus. Martha had been his legal mother at birth, but had given the child in adoption to Mary.

If three women could have claims of varying sorts to motherhood, four men could in different ways be called his father. The donor of the sperm with which the ovum was fertilized, and the three husbands – of Elizabeth, Martha, and Mary – all had claims to the title.

Legal issues were involved: Martha's father's will had left property to the 'heirs of her body'. Was Phil, whom she had carried in her uterus, her heir? What kind of access was the court to give to the natural mothers? If Phil died, which of his parents would be his legal heirs? Through which of his parents had Phil acquired his heart condition, or was it the result of genetic defects in one of them or of drugs taken by either of his natural mothers? Had any of these parents, their physicians, or laboratory technicians involved in the artificial fertilization, been negligent? If Phil was to have a right of action against any of his parents or their medical advisers, which parents could most appropriately be his guardians for the action?

Jack was the product of an artificial insemination. At the time of his birth no adequate register had been maintained by medical authorities on the number of times the same sperm had been used. Thousands of citizens had been conceived by artificial insemination, and it was now possible for half brothers and sisters to marry without knowing about their relationship. When the records were checked, Jack found that he and his wife were conceived through sperm from the same donor. The health department sought the annulment of marriages such as theirs, or alternatively the compulsory sterilization of one spouse or the other. The legitimacy of children already born of such marriages presented another legal problem in the event of the annulment of the marriages.

These sorts of complications are not wild speculations. The first major report of the authoritative *New England Journal of Medicine*, released in 1979, revealed that only 249 of 711 doctors questioned in the US could say how many times they had used the same sperm.

Helen was a spastic. She was one of a batch of eight full-term test-tube babies brought into existence by a doctor in Canada in 1989, a technique practised in many countries. In 1961, a doctor in Italy was reported to have grown an embryo in a test-tube for a month and then ended its life. Doctors in the US had, by slow degrees, extended the period to four months. When a doctor in Japan had grown a foetus to full term in the laboratory, the lawyers were thrown into confusion. When did the child become a human being? What credentials must doctors have to produce babies in the laboratory? Was there to be a 'decantation' certificate? Was it necessary to have a period of observation, to check if any serious abnormalities showed up before the birth was certified? What was to be done if there were a major defect resulting from the laboratory procedures? Up to what pre- or postnatal age was it acceptable to dispose of imperfect babies? Would secret foetus cultivation be carried out in the backyard laboratories of unethical doctors? How could test-tube babies be protected by the law?

The elaborate constitutional provisions by which Japan guarantees human rights to every citizen at once became the subject of heated debate. The United Nations debated the issue and the WHO issued guidelines subjecting the procedure to strict limitations and surveillance: test-tube babies could only be produced by strictly licensed doctors, on parental request and with a permit from the state, given after investigation by a representative committee of scientists, lawyers and lay people. The technology had become accessible to less responsible people, however, and, in some countries, babies were being produced before all the issues had been clarified.

Canada had adopted the WHO guidelines and Helen had been produced on a permit. A 'decantation' certificate had been issued after 280 days and a full birth certificate after a further observation period of a month. Her spastic condition had become apparent only in her third year and was growing acutely worse. Investigation had revealed that defective laboratory procedures were responsible for her condition, and that she was one of several hundred similar children in Canada.

A huge corporation of the 1990s, which owns nuclear reactors, has not been pleased with the readiness of some of its employees to criticize its safety precautions. True, all employees have been carefully screened before appointment: they have been psychoanalysed and their political leanings investigated. But there is unease on the part of management, for protest is uncomfortable and expensive.

The company provides housing for its employees. The housing is so professionally 'bugged' that employees are quite unable to know when and how they are under surveillance. Hair-thin transmitters concealed behind wallpaper, laser beams bounced off windowpanes, and miniature instruments built into the floorboards record and transmit a flood of information denying any concept of privacy.

The danger to employees thus spied upon is not merely loss of employment. The law has long provided other sanctions, such as fines and long terms of imprisonment, to those who obstruct the nuclear industry, which has become essential to the economy and, as the risk of terrorism grows, dangerous. Legislation imposes the strictest security measures: people may be arrested on suspicion, held without trial, and their houses searched and property seized.

Trade unionism is all but banned in the industry; any disruptions to work are considered subversive. A special atomic constabulary carries arms and may arrest on suspicion. The burden of proof is reversed, and the accused must prove their innocence if their cases come up for trial. Members of the government or the atomic agency authority are immune from consequences in the event of wrongful arrest or detention. Justification for such stringencies is claimed on the basis that, as in the Australian *Atomic Energy Act* of 1953, such provisions have existed from the beginning of the development of nuclear power.

No employee dares to come into conflict with that powerful combination – bureaucracy, high commerce and the military – which operates the nuclear industry. All these powerful entities, any one of them strong enough to hold any citizen at bay, have a conglomeration of power which it is idle to resist. Joe Bloggs, entering into a contract of service with them, is, in theory, a free man entering of his own free will and on terms to which he has freely consented. In practice, the law could not be further from reality, and the lawyers have learnt that legal regulation is an academic exercise. Both lawyer and citizen have resigned themselves to this erosion of democratic principle.

The obsession with security is pervasive. At the borders of every country, international and national atomic energy agency inspectors are on duty armed with powers of search and arrest. They also have the right of entry into customs and postal offices and the right of inspection of all parcels coming into the country. The death penalty for infringements of these laws are on the statute books of many countries, including some which have long traditions of the rule of law. The sentence is not infrequently carried out.

In 1989 a legal debate had been conducted on the protections demanded by the computer industry for communications systems, data banks and computers. These industries demanded that their legal protections be the same as those of the nuclear industry: arrest on suspicion, an armed constabulary, tapping of telephone calls, extended terms of imprisonment, reversal of the burden of proof. Society had grown so dependent on computers that all public activity would grind to a halt if a key computer were hijacked. Private and public data networks, video conference facilities carrying the intimate secrets of big business, the growing alliance between the telecommunication network and the mass media, through the growth of cable telecommunication systems and video display and facsimile terminals, all provided a potent argument in favour of such powers: society was now far more dependent on these industries. Computers were guarded with the same care and stringencies as were heads of state. Whoever disrupted a computer or took possession of a computer centre could hold an entire community to ransom and bring commercial and governmental operations to a standstill. It was an offence, punishable by long-term prison sentences, to harm communication operations of the computer companies and mass market.

Indeed, the statute books of 1999 contain many pieces of legislation which would look strange to the liberal-minded lawyers of the 1970s or early 1980s. Shortages of resources, such as petrol, natural gas and copper, have forced the evolution of controls for their use, and a bureaucracy with greatly enhanced powers has administered the regulations with a heavy hand. Permits are required for activities which were unthinkable as the subject of controls until the early 1980s. The legislative response to possible terrorism involves arrest, search, seizure, prolonged interrogation, or imprisonment without trial. Security regulations on railways and public transport and in government and business offices are pervasive and severe. Security has become an obsession.

These are no fanciful scenarios. They depict the legal problems latent in contemporary scientific knowledge.

The world of 1999 presents strange new legal phenomena. The dangers to legal protections are visible. Whether they can be averted or mitigated depends on the foresight and concern we display now.

Chapter 2

Human Rights, Law and Technology

All of the problems foreshadowed in the first chapter have an intimate relationship with technology, human rights and the law. In addressing such problems we need to deal with the relationship between human rights and law and between those two concepts and technology.

Law in the common law countries (that is, where the English common law is the basis of the legal system, as in Australia and the US) consists principally of statute law and judge-made law. The former are enactments by the legislature setting out the law on specific matters. The latter are the principles underlying judicial decisions of the superior courts, which are treated as binding in subsequent cases involving similar issues. These two principal sources of law, commonly termed 'black letter' law, reduce to written form the bulk of the common law legal systems.

Although the legislature is free to enact such legislation as it pleases (except where a constitution or bill of rights circumscribes its power), the judges are theoretically not free to make law as they please. They are bound by statute law and previous decisions. A legal fiction which still holds in common law jurisdictions has it that judges are only drawing on a pre-existing body of common law and that when they formulate a new principle, they are, in theory, only drawing on old principles. Nobody believes today that there is such an inexhaustible reservoir of legal principles, for we all know that many decisions embody new principles which are formulated by judges. There is an attempt in the judgments, however, to justify those principles on the basis of earlier decisions. In many cases, this is only a formal exercise. The reality is that new law is being made.

From what source do legislature and judiciary draw their inspiration for new formulations of law? The legislature attempts, as best it can, to give effect to the wishes of the electorate, thus often translating these wishes into law. In a system of indirect democracy, it is not always possible for the legislature to mirror exactly the community's wishes and sentiments, and it often happens that legislation is passed which might not have the support of a majority of the community. But, in theory, this is what the legislature seeks to do. The judges, to the extent that they are making law, likewise reflect, consciously or unconsciously, the moral sentiments of the community.

A further question arises about the sources from which the community's sentiments are drawn. The factors contributing to the attitudes of a community include religion, tradition, custom, the needs of commerce, political exigencies, and basic philosophical tenets, to name a few. These factors in varying combinations often colour people's approach to new problems. Matters of abortion, euthanasia, privacy and environmental protection, for example, engage the attention of the legislature and the courts from time to time and, in various jurisdictions and in differing degrees, become the subject of the law. Where, as in Australia, there is an active and responsive Law Reform Commission, a better apparatus exists than otherwise for assessing public attitudes.

Some of the community's values have, over the last two centuries, in particular, been translated into law in the form of written constitutions, such as the US one, as well as in various statutory provisions and judicial decisions. One of their central themes is the dignity and integrity of the individual. In the US, this was translated into practical terms in the bill of rights in such provisions as the fourteenth amendment. In the UK, and in countries without a bill of rights, provisions to protect a person's dignity and liberty are principally found in the body of judicial decisions that have been handed down over the years. Important constitutional documents such as Magna Carta, 1215, and the Declaration of Rights, 1689, have helped to build up a climate of respect for individual liberty. Other countries have a varying mix between constitutional provisions and judicial decisions.

The concept of human rights is a concept distinct from the concept of law, for human rights exist at the level of philosophy rather than the law. True, they are constantly in the process of translation into law, but the concept of human rights is not dependent on legal formulation or enactment for its validity. When the human right to life is translated in the US constitution into the fourteenth amendment, it becomes law and is then both a matter of human rights and of legal provision. There are, however, many matters of human rights which have not been translated into law. Indeed the world's foremost human rights document, the Universal Declaration of Human Rights, is not law, but a set of aspirations.

Since the Universal Declaration, there has been a burst of human rights activities. Declarations such as the Declaration on the Rights of the Child (1959), on Discrimination Against Women (1967), and on the Rights of Mentally Retarded Persons (1971) are some of the formal human rights declarations which have followed. And in the twin covenants on Economic, Social and Cultural Rights and on Social and Political Rights of 1966, the notion of human rights has been expanded to new fields, and new machinery to give effect to some of the rights proclaimed in the Universal Declaration has been established.

In recent years, as increasing emphasis is given to hitherto unexplored facets of the human right of life, there has been growing discussion internationally of such matters as the beginning and end of life, the right to health as an adjunct to the right to life, the right to safe conditions of work, the right to a pure and unpolluted environment, the right to freedom from medical experimentation, the right to freedom from manipulation of the mind and the right to privacy. This is the philosophical setting in which the current human rights discourse is cast. There is a confluence here of three streams of activity: human rights thinking, legal regulation, and technological advance. As science keeps increasing our ability to interfere with human beings and nature, increasing numbers of issues surface for which earlier legal regulation does not have the answer and for which human rights doctrine needs to be developed.

Table 2.1 sets out the technological advances which will denigrate basic human rights unless the law expands to deal with the problems they pose.

Table 2.1

Human Dignity

Provisions

Preamble to the Universal Declaration (recognition of the inherent dignity of all members of the human family is the foundation of freedom, justice and peace in the world.

Article 1 — All human beings are born free and equal in dignity and rights . . .

Article 5 — No one shall be subjected to . . . degrading treatment.

Article 6 — Everyone has the right to recognition everywhere as a person before the law.

Article 29(1) — 'Free and full development of . . . personality' is a basic value.

Sources of Possible Denigration

Foetal experimentation	Enzyme engineering
Human experimentation	Sale of human tissue
Embryo transplantation	Screening procedures
In vitro fertilization	Psychosurgery
Foetus farms	Behaviour therapy
Sperm and ova banks	Electroconvulsive therapy
Combinations of human and	Personality tests
other genetic material	Torture techniques
Selective breeding	Use of drugs in
Genetic structuring of	interrogation
humans	Surveillance devices
Preselection of sex	Euthanasia techniques
Societal breeding	Machine decision making
Unwanted surgery	Computerized regimentation
Sale and hire of organs	of society
Organ transplants	Data bank infringements of
	privacy

Freedom of Thought

Provisions
Article 18 — Everyone has the right to freedom of thought, conscience and religion.
Article 19 — Everyone has the right to freedom of opinion . . . this right includes freedom to hold opinions without interference.

Sources of Possible Denigration

Psychosurgery
Chemical controls of the mind
Data banks
Use of drugs in interrogation
Psychotherapy
Personality tests
Behaviour therapy

Electroconvulsive therapy
Mind conditioning through media technologies, e.g. subliminal advertising, advertising directed at children
Surveillance devices
Repression of anti-nuclear protest

Right to Life

Provisions
Article 3 — Everyone has the right to life . . .

Sources of Possible Denigration

Abortion
In vitro fertilization
Embryo transplantation
Human experimentation
Foetal experimentation
Organ transplants
Unwanted surgery

Euthanasia techniques
Technological terrorism, e.g. nuclear
Torture techniques
Military technology, e.g. chemical, germ, nuclear.

Right to Bodily Security

Provisions

Article 3 — Everyone has a right to . . . security of person.
Article 5 — No one shall be subjected to torture or to cruel, inhuman or degrading treatment or punishment.

Sources of Possible Denigration

Torture techniques
Organ transplants
Sale and hire of organs
Sale of human tissue
Euthanasia techniques
Unwanted surgery

Human experimentation
Foetal experimentation
Abortion
Military technology
Nuclear terrorism

Right to Health

Provisions

Article 25(1) — Everyone has the right to a standard of living adequate for the health and well-being of himself and of his family . . . including . . . medical care.
Article 23(1) — Everyone has the right to . . . favourable conditions of work.

Sources of Possible Denigration

Recombinant DNA experimentation
Military technology
Chemical hazards in industry
Euthanasia
Human experimentation
Organ transplants
Unwanted surgery
Untested drugs, e.g. thalidomide
Genetic engineering
In vitro fertilization

Psychosurgery
Behaviour therapy
Torture techniques
Depletion of the ozone layer
Atmospheric pollution through discharge of industrial waste
Heat pollution
Noise pollution
Chemical pollution
Nuclear pollution
Chemical controls of the mind

Privacy

Provisions
Article 12 — No one shall be subject to arbitrary interference with his or her privacy.

Sources of Possible Denigration

Computer technology
The technology of computer crime
Surveillance devices
Media technology
Human experimentation
Use of drugs in interrogation
Artificial insemination
Cloning

Sperm and ova banks
Screening procedures
Personality tests
Mind manipulation
Psychotherapy
Psychosurgery
Chemical controls of the mind
Behaviour therapy

Rights of Marriage and Procreation

Provisions
Article 16(1) — Men and women of full age, without any limitation due to race, nationality or religion, have the right to marry and to found a family.

Sources of Possible Denigration

Sperm and ova banks
In vitro fertilization
Embryo transplantation
AID procedures
Genetic engineering
Screening procedures
Sale of organs

Organ transplants, e.g. testes, Fallopian tubes
Nuclear pollution
Untested chemicals in industry
Radiation hazards, e.g. infra ray cookers
Pesticides

Protection of Motherhood and Childhood

Provisions
Article 25(2) — Motherhood and childhood are entitled to special care and assistance.

Sources of Possible Denigration

Foetal experimentation	Genetic engineering
Foetus farms	Amniocentesis and
In vitro fertilization	foetoscopy
Embryo transplantation	Abortion
AID procedures	Preselection of foetal sex

Right to Cultural Life

Provisions
Article 27.1 — Everyone has the right freely to participate in the cultural life of the community, to enjoy the arts and to share in scientific advancement and its benefits.

Sources of Possible Denigration

Media technologies for	Scientific secrecy
cultural indoctrination and	Computerized regimentation
saturation	of society
Monopolies	Surveillance devices
Intellectual property in	Invasions of privacy
scientific knowledge	

Right to Work

Provisions
Article 23.1 — Everyone has the right to work, to free choice of employment, to just and favourable conditions of work and to protection against unemployment.

Sources of Possible Denigration

Personality tests	Data banks
Screening procedures	Computerization of industry

I will not attempt to question the enormous benefits science has so far conferred on humanity. Nor will I attempt to question its undoubted potential for leading humanity to that world of plenty which has long been its dream. But I will question whether society is sufficiently alert to the dangers in the path of technological advancement, and whether lawyers have been properly vigilant. I will also question whether legal concepts are adequate to take the thrust of these new directions in science, and whether human rights are adequately protected against the abuse of scientific knowledge.

My thesis is that the dangers which technology raises are distinguishable from all others which legal systems have ever faced. I shall argue that their resolution is urgent and that few tasks are worthier of concerted endeavour.

In reconciling the conflicting interests in this technological age, the law has a basic duty to protect every individual's personality, health, freedom, and dignity, and to be sensitive to current human rights thinking on these issues. It must monitor the new technology against abuse. It must work out its responses to the novel conflicts of interests that will arise.

Figure 2.1 represents the continuous interaction of the law and the forces surrounding it. It represents the dynamism expected of the law, which has been slow in forthcoming.

Irreversibility of a course once taken is one of the law's cardinal difficulties in its confrontation with science. Modern technology's effects are often for ever. It threatens the environment with irreversible pollution, brings within human reach the power of structuring people, makes nuclear terrorism a reality for all time, and produces drugs which can paralyse the world. Nothing this or future generations can do can take this knowledge away from mankind. Like nuclear wastes, which will be with us for at least 20,000 years, this information will be with us forever.

We are privileged to live in the one remaining age when something can be done. In our children's time it will be too late, if it is not too late already. If the present slide towards uncontrollability should continue for another decade, technology will have mastered us.

Every invention that has given us power over our environ-

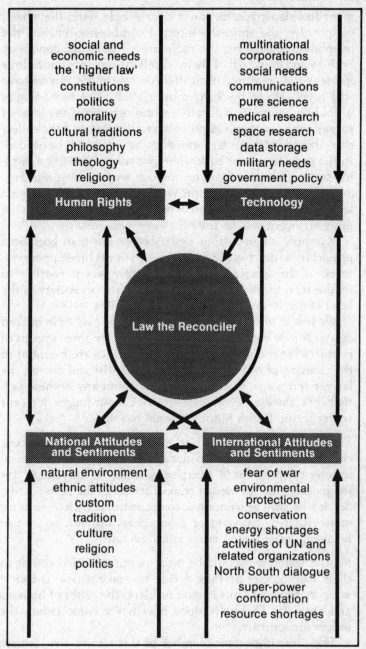

social and
economic needs
the 'higher law'
constitutions
politics
morality
cultural traditions
philosophy
theology
religion

multinational
corporations
social needs
communications
pure science
medical research
space research
data storage
military needs
government policy

Human Rights ↔ **Technology**

Law the Reconciler

**National Attitudes
and Sentiments** ↔ **International Attitudes
and Sentiments**

natural environment
ethnic attitudes
custom
tradition
culture
religion
politics

fear of war
environmental
protection
conservation
energy shortages
activities of UN and
related organizations
North South dialogue
super-power
confrontation
resource shortages

Figure 2.1

ment has also given us power over people. Fire, the wheel, gunpowder, the ship, the internal combustion engine, the telephone, telegraphy, the radio are all powerful conquests both *by* and *of* us. All of them, excellent servants but callous masters, have required us to alter our way of life, but we have still been able to hold them on a leash. The technologies unfolding before us will raise technology above the level of subservience to people. Controls, regulations, and the collective strength of the international community will be needed. In the process, we are back where we started, for in attempting to gain freedom from technology we have lost our freedom; in attempting to improve the quality of life through technology we have debased it. The longer we delay, the more stringent will be the necessary measures.

It is now a truism that never before has man been able physically to destroy his environment, or his life-support systems, or the species itself. Never before was it possible to reduce man to the level of an object or human society to the level of a systems programmer's blueprint.

We live in an age when old moral guidelines have broken down. A new course must be set.[1] There are three groups of people whose knowledge, views and wishes are essential to the charting of our new course: the scientist and doctor, the lawyer and judge, and lay people. Without any of these participants, the dialogue breaks down. Of our judges, a recent writer in the *British Medical Journal* has said:

These are busy times for our black-robed Judges as they toil in their chambers, poring over dusty volumes and burning the midnight oil to solve the problems of a perplexing world ... Increasingly it is the Judges – not the elected representatives of the people – who decide who shall be terminated, compensated, reinstated, executed or resuscitated, vivisected or desegregated, dialysed, certified or involuntarily medicated, mercy killed, educated ...[2]

Similar statements could be made of our scientists toiling in their laboratories as they decide to make a new chemical weapon, grow a foetus *in vitro* or blend the genes of humans and animals. These decisions may never come before the judges for scrutiny.

The most important member of this trinity, the layman,

remains strangely silent although he is the party most concerned and the legitimate source of authority for all socially
oriented decision making. To speak figuratively in the
language of administrative law, he is entitled to ask those
who decide these matters for him, '*Quo warranto?*', – 'What
is your authority?' When a decision is given, he is entitled
to ask that it be reviewed at the bar of public opinion. He
must increasingly seek writs restraining various forms of governmental and scientific action. He must seek orders compelling various authorities to disclose information and perform other acts (analogous to the writ of Mandamus). For
members of the public to perform these functions, they need
to be well informed about the scientific and human rights
issues with which they are entangled.

Chapter 3

Inadequacies of the Law

The world of Anglo-American law is dominated by the concept of adversarial litigation. Judges are umpires deciding which of two parties should win according to the formal rules of the game. They are not determining truth as they see it but determining who should win. The parties seek victory rather than truth.

In the increasing numbers of disputes involving scientific testimony, the adversary system is constantly demonstrating its unsuitability.

Within limits, a party to an adversarial proceeding tends to keep away from court such evidence or witnesses as may not favour his or her cause. The court is largely content with the parties' choice of witnesses, rarely calling them on its own, and often knows little of the available evidence not placed before it. The collection of the fullest information on the topic under investigation is remote from the objectives of the court.

Technical rules of procedure do not help in determining whether to halt some dangerous activity such as the release of an untried chemical or the escape of dangerous viruses into the biosphere.

The forensic presentation tends to overstress and overstate 'winning' points and propositions. The scientific presentation is more detached and restrained. The former covers even favourable ground selectively; the latter gives an overall coverage to all relevant material.

Experienced presentation is always at a premium and often plays an unbalanced part in determining the result. Strategy and court craft become valued in themselves.

Scientific fact finders demand a high level of certainty and accuracy for their conclusions. The nature of the judicial process is such that courts have traditionally been content with such vague formulae as 'proof by a balance of probability' in civil litigation and 'proof beyond reasonable doubt' in criminal cases. Judges in the adversarial system instinctively apply these formulae, especially the first, if the litigation does not have a criminal character. For scientific fact finding this is totally inadequate.

Adversarial litigation does not ordinarily allow the public to be represented as a third affected party. The point was made many years ago, in relation to safety determinations in nuclear power licensing, that both in the course of the licensing process and after the decision the public had no adequate opportunity of representation.[1] This observation would also apply to formal court proceedings.

Adversarial proceedings are structured to produce a finding which is effective *between the two parties*. It does not bind anyone else. Scientific fact finding must hold for the whole community.

A rule of evidence, for example, may decree that the contents of a document shall not be proved except by producing the document. The purpose of adversary proceedings is well served by this procedure, but the purpose of finding the truth is not, because the evidence in the document, even if it is not produced, may be vital.

Likewise, rules regarding the witnessing, stamping, or certification of a document can result in the exclusion of vital evidence for lack of compliance with prescribed formalities.

Another large category of rules, the rules of estoppel, prevent parties from making assertions contrary to their earlier assertions, if other parties have acted on them. A party who has earlier taken up a certain position is thus held bound to it whether that position is true or false. Such a method employed in the scientific field can be quite silly.

A further weakness of legal method, as it concerns scientific matters, is in its reliance on precedent.

The adversary system thus seems entirely lacking in the flexibility of method necessary for the assessment of a constantly advancing body of knowledge. To quote an Australian jurist:

... scientific material is always provisional and is constantly becoming out-of-date, so that yesterday's truth is today's error. Unfortunately, however, in the law yesterday's belief, when embodied in a binding precedent, becomes authority for today. Hence courts may, with the best of intentions, find themselves unwillingly perpetuating what the world of science now regards as error.[2]

Like the ancient doctrine of precedent, the ancient doctrine of national sovereignty is inadequate in the scientific age.

The narrowly nationalistic view, on which legal systems are structured, is proving to be completely inadequate for handling modern technology. Nuclear physics, transborder data flow, satellite communication, recombinant DNA research, the chemicals explosion, pollution, aerial navigation, space research are all proving that the old nation-based jurisprudence is totally inadequate without international regulation.

Similar difficulties result from outmoded concepts of private property in knowledge.

Although inventors are clearly entitled to some financial reward for their work and originality, the notion of absolute proprietorship is outmoded. The classic illustration is that of the discoverer of a cancer cure who charges $10,000 for a course of treatment. True, he or she must have rewards, but society likewise has an interest in the discovery. New techniques of food production being withheld while thousands starve is another illustration. The limits of the respective rights of the discoverer and of society will never be adequately worked out as long as the principle of exclusive private property in knowledge continues.

The thalidomide case was an interesting illustration of the manner in which private proprietary interests can defeat the public interest. In that case, Distillers Ltd, the manufacturers of the drug which caused deformities in numerous children whose mothers had used it during pregnancy, were sued by parents. A lengthy period of negotiations followed, without the case proceeding to trial. *The Sunday Times* began a series of articles about thalidomide one of which was to deal with the history of the testing, manufacture and marketing of the drug. The attorney general obtained an injunction restraining publication of the article on the ground that it would constitute a contempt of court. The High Court granted the injunction, the Court of Appeal refused it, the House of Lords restored the injunction, and it was only on further appeal to the European Court of Human Rights that the injunction was refused and publication permitted. The court, by a majority of eleven votes to nine, held that the restraint on publication was not justified. The European Court held that the thalidomide disaster was a matter of undisputed public concern and that the public and the families of the victims had a right to be properly informed. As Lord Denning had observed in the Court of Appeal, this was a case where the public interest counterbalanced the private interest of the parties.

As *The Sunday Times* said in an editorial on the subject, 'For fourteen years . . . this disaster has languished under a system of legal censorship that is archaically against the public interest.'[3]

Technologies of all descriptions – nuclear, chemical, and microbiological in particular – are tampering with the rights of the unborn, but the law has been tardy in evolving concepts to deal with them. The thalidomide case has shown how ill equipped the law is, both in substance and procedure, to deal with these questions. The protection of the thousands of unborn children injured by the chemicals explosion or nuclear radiation and the claims by unborn generations for genetic damage have not reached the threshold of legal planning. Beyond a few sporadic recognitions of rights of the unborn, the law has shown great nervousness in protecting any but those who are already conceived (*en ventre sa mère*).

Legal inability to contain and control technological inroads is compounded by the concept of corporate anonymity, which enables their perpetrators to escape unscathed. The foisting of dangerous and untested products on the public, pollution of the sea and the atmosphere, and computer crime are some of the areas where the law is unable to track down offenders.

Likewise, the long-distance scanner, the bug, the secret transmitter, and the computer have rendered the concepts of

privacy and physical trespass outmoded, and the law is strug-
gling to formulate new concepts, unaided by any guidance
of significance from traditional common law.

On 24 July 1979, the media carried reports of the stock-
piling by the US of a hallucinogenic drug, BZ, which could
paralyse and reduce to helplessness 40,000 million people
(ten times the world's population) for several days. Situations such as this which threaten the very future of
humanity are appearing in a dozen areas of science, but
laissez-faire principles in scientific research are still accepted
in the legal system. Scientists are within reach of being able
to fabricate desired types of humans, mind manipulation
techniques are being used to impair the integrity of the
human mind, and nuclear proliferation unleashes possibilities of terrorism and surveillance. But in all these fields, lawyers have been slow to adjust their thinking. In the words
of Bertrand Russell:

... unless something rather drastic is done under the leadership or
through the inspiration of some part of the scientific world, the
human race, like the Gadarene swine, will rush down a steep place
to destruction in blind ignorance of the fate which scientific skill
has prepared for it.[4]

'It seems clear', says sociologist Jacques Ellul, a pioneer in
this field, 'that we cannot rely on the courts alone to protect
society against fast-moving technological development.
Judge-made rules of law always come after, and usually long
after, the potential for injury has been demonstrated.'[5]

The courts as presently structured are scarcely competent
to assess the long-range effects of a particular scientific or
technological innovation. The task calls for a degree of
informed skill in prediction and judgment which is beyond
the traditional expertise of courts. Social planning, on the
other hand, functions in the area of the foreseen rather than
the known and concerns itself with the fashioning of benefits
rather than the redress of injury. Its technique is not the resolution of disputes after they occur, but the formulation of
procedures to prevent their occurrence.

Moreover, disputes involving a scientific component come
increasingly before the courts, and a great proportion of these

depend for their eventual determination upon a value judgment. A judge of the US Court of Appeals, in drawing attention to this aspect, enumerated some of the questions coming
before his court for decision.[6] They involved the ecological
effects of building a pipeline to bring oil across the Atlantic
tundra; the management of radioactive wastes from nuclear
reactors; and the banning of DDT or Concorde SST or lead
in gasoline.

Each of these questions involves a value judgment which
needs to be based on scientific fact. The ecological preservation of the tundra needs to be balanced against society's
need for oil; the hazards of radioactivity to future generations
against the urgent energy needs of the present; the economic
advantages of a pesticide against its medical disadvantages;
the advantages of speed against the disadvantages of the sonic
boom; the advantage of a smoother fuel against the disadvan-
tage of atmospheric pollution.

Value judgments, resource allocations, and community
priorities in matters of this nature are scarcely questions
which the courts have the mandate, the competence, or the
machinery to handle.

The advent of science and technology into the mechanics
of the trial has also indirectly weakened some of the legal attitudes which built protective safeguards around people and
their rights.

There is increasingly a belief that many of the matters
which formerly lay in the sphere of judicial discretion can
now be entrusted to mechanical devices or scientific rules,
such as speed detectors, breathalyzers, videotapes, handwriting analyses, scent detectors, mathematical calculations
of probability, and computers. The reality is that these
devices are useful within limits, but that they are no substitute for judicial discretion. Handwriting 'science' can identify a finger print on a knife but cannot tell us whether the
knife of an innocent person was planted at the scene of the
crime. The laws of mathematical probability may be wrongly
applied to a case where an assailant's characteristics are
matched with those of an accused,[7] breathalyzers can be in-
accurate, and speed detectors can be tampered with.

The growth in the use of such devices, however, has undermined some of the basic principles of common law. Where the machine indicates guilt, for example, there is almost automatically a shifting of the burden of proof. The prosecution can now put forward the machine evidence and sit back, challenging the accused to prove his or her innocence. As every motorist knows, who seeks to challenge a speedometer or breathalyzer conclusion, the contention that the machine was faulty, even if it were, often imposes an impossible burden of proof on the challenger. It involves evidence which is either in the exclusive possession of the prosecutor or which is of a degree of sophistication not within his or her reach. The defendant tends therefore to capitulate to the machine, in negation of his or her common law rights.

Another erosion of basic rights results from the need imposed by such machines to submit the citizen to their application. The common law principle that people are not obliged to give evidence that might incriminate them thereby stands jeopardized, and whether it is a finger print, a breathalyzer test, a voice sample, or a blood test, submission becomes an obligation and refusal a virtual proof of guilt.

Furthermore, the technicalities of scientific evidence often tend to be of great complexity. Questions such as blood grouping, in a complicated trial, may involve expert scientific evidence on the very frontiers of scientific knowledge. Sophisticated experiments or scientific hypotheses may need to be evaluated which would require weeks of lectures to medical or science students.

An excellent example of the sophisticated technologies that are now invoked for purposes of proof in judicial proceedings was given by the Chamberlain murder trial which attracted world attention in 1982. In this case, the mother of a nine and a half-week-old baby was charged with its murder. The body was never found and the defence claimed that the baby had been carried away and devoured by a dingo, a species of Australian wild dog found in the Ayers Rock area, where the baby disappeared. The case is highly interesting and so illustrative that it warrants special examination.

The circumstantial evidence led by the prosecution depended heavily on the most advanced developments in immunology and protein chemistry. Immunology concerns itself with animal reactions to foreign substances; protein chemistry centres on the identification of the constituents of living things by chemical means. These two branches of science were invoked to solve the problem of matching the bloodstains found in the Chamberlains' car with the blood of Azaria, the baby alleged to have been murdered. This was important, as a key question in the case was whether the bloodstains detected in the car came from Azaria or from some other person, in particular, an injured passenger transported in the car to hospital on an earlier occasion. The distinction between adult haemoglobin and foetal haemoglobin was vital for this purpose, as babies' blood, until the age of six months, contains about 25 per cent foetal and 75 per cent adult haemoglobin. (Haemoglobin is the red oxygen-carrying pigment in the red cells of the blood.) The high percentage of foetal haemoglobin in these infants is a carryover from the foetal stage, for foetal haemoglobin has superior oxygen-collecting capabilities, necessary for competing with the mother's blood for the oxygen in her body.

Immunology offered a means of investigating the blood samples through the use of antisera. Serum is the liquid part of blood left after blood has clotted, and antiserum is the serum obtained from an animal that has been injected with a foreign substance such as foetal or adult human blood. Antisera react with blood samples in a way that helps to identify the latter. This can be observed in sophisticated tests which must be carefully planned to eliminate all other possibilities.

Protein chemistry offered a means of further individual identification of the blood by using a genetic marker not unlike those employed in paternity suits for matching the blood of offspring and father. In this case, the marker used was an isoenzyme, phosphoglucomutase (PGM, an agent responsible for processing sugar in the body) which differs sufficiently in human subjects to enable identification of blood as being from a particular group of individuals. PGM can only be identified in its different variations by the most sophisticated and advanced biotechnology, such as isoelectric focusing, the results of which were actually led in evidence in the case.

Clearly, the scientific evidence involved was of a degree of sophistication well beyond the ability of average lay people to grasp fully. The tests discussed and used in this case take us to the frontiers of scientific knowledge in these fields; indeed, some of them may require explanation to scientific experts.

Irrespective of the results of a case, factors such as these must make lawyers, scientists and lay people think about the machinery available under current legal structures for assessing such evidence. The Chamberlain case, with its many days of abstruse scientific evidence, is a useful warning of a general problem which will escalate with the increasing use of high technology for purposes of proof in court.

Whatever people's theoretical rights may be, their true content is determined to a large extent by the procedures available for their assertion and enforcement. These procedures have always involved a mix of the logical and the discretionary. The former is cold, impersonal, incapable of the requisite nuances and often unrelated to reality. The latter, by its flexibility, has furnished the principal driving force for the development of legal systems and bodies of rights. The advent of technology is fast changing the character of the mix. Scientific reasoning, a useful catalyst in moderation, is tending to become dominant, resulting in a diminution of the concepts of individuality and human rights.

As the Australian Law Reform Commission has observed:

New questions are raised regarding the proper faith that may be put by the law in machines, given that the consequences may visit criminal penalties on the accused. These questions point the way for other likely advances in the law in years to come. It is, therefore, important that at the outset we should get right our approach to these novel legal developments.[8]

Law reform in Australia to meet new technological developments labours under certain special handicaps not faced by many other countries. One of these arises from Australia's constitutional structure. For a country with a population of fifteen million, which is small by world standards, there are seven units of government, each with its own legislature and judiciary. Legal principles can vary from state to state, and there can be disputes whether a particular matter is within state or commonwealth power. A large amount of legal manpower is wasted on separate law reform commissions for the states and the commonwealth government. Uniform progress to meet new legal and human rights problems is an impossibility.

In the area of technology, in particular, the legal and human rights problems that arise are often not state but national ones. State regulation serves little purpose if there is no overall national approach. Yet there is no power for the federal government to achieve national law reform to cope, for example, with issues such as those in the bioethical field.

One of the principal obstacles to Australia's legal ability to cope with technological change is this archaic and inefficient structure. But, as the chairman of the Australian Law Reform Commission recently observed, on all their law reform bodies Australians spend an average of only 10 cents a person a year – a total of only $1.5 million.[9]

Chapter 4
The Human Body

For humanitarian achievement, medical science stands high among all fields of intellectual endeavour. Inveterate scourges of mankind, such as smallpox, leprosy and polio, have been conquered or brought under control. The healing scalpel works its miracles from the macro-organ transplant to the delicate field of micro-surgery. Pain is suppressed and controlled. Longevity has been significantly increased. Presiding over all these activities is a humane medical profession, as skilled as it is dedicated.

But there is an attendant gloom. The ability to heal the body brings with it an ability to tinker, to fabricate, to mould, and even to interfere with the processes of creation and termination of life. Powers of healing grow into powers of control.

In this development there lies more than an ordinary share of peril to liberty, for it is to the human body that most basic legal and human rights protections are anchored.

From an inexhaustible list, only some of the danger areas can be singled out for illustration. These fall into three broad groups: patients' rights, organ and tissue transplants, and birth and procreation.

In September 1978, the World Health Organization held a conference from which emerged the Declaration of Alma Ata which began as follows: 'The conference strongly reaffirms that health, which is a state of complete physical, mental and social well-being and not merely the absence of disease or infirmity, is a fundamental human right.' The absence of disease or infirmity is no longer an expectation but a right.

Patients' Rights
Psychosurgery

In 1972, Dr Jose Delgado, a pioneer in psychosurgical research, went into a bull ring in the path of a charging bull. Using remote control to activate electrodes implanted by him in the bull's brain, he calmed the animal's rage and halted it in its tracks. This raised speculation about the possible application of such techniques to humans.

Delgado was illustrating only one of a multitude of techniques science has made available for influencing the workings of the mammalian brain. Psychosurgery, electroconvulsive therapy, drug therapy, psychotherapy, and behaviour therapy are others. They all raise ethical and human rights issues which penetrate the Universal Declaration's pronouncements on the dignity of human beings (Article 1), their freedom from degrading treatment (Article 5), their recognition as people (Article 6), their rights to privacy (Article 12), their right to freedom of thought and opinion (Article 18), their right to health (Article 25(1)), and their right to the full development of their personalities (Article 29(1)).

Noting the possibilities of one of these techniques Albert Rosenfeld observed:

One can easily imagine people in the future wearing self-stimulating electrodes (it might even become the 'in' thing to do) which might render the wearer sexually potent at any time; that might put him to sleep or keep him awake, according to his need; that might curb his appetite if he wanted to lose weight; that might relieve him of pain; that might give him courage when he was fearful or render him tranquil when he was enraged.[1]

Electric stimulation of the brain can induce motor movements such as walking, although not as yet with sufficient sophistication to create a scenario of 'men with intra-cerebral electrodes engaged in all kinds of mischief under the perverse guidance of radio waves sent by some evil scientist'.[2]

External intrusions into the human brain raise questions about human identity. A split-brain operation, by which the principal connections between the two brain hemispheres are severed to prevent the spread of epileptic seizures from one side of the brain to the other, reveals some peculiar phenomena. If a picture is shown to the patient on the left side of his visual field, that information is transmitted to the right side of the brain, and since the speech centre is in the left half of the brain which sensed nothing, he will be unable to describe the picture verbally. Yet his left hand, which is controlled by the right half of his brain, can pick up the object. Indeed, it is possible to teach the two halves different things, with no transmission between them of the information they have received. In 1969, experiments on a chimpanzee showed that automatic learning is possible by directly feeding signals into specific parts of the brain.

Chemical techniques are other instruments for mind control. Minutely controlled doses of chemicals can induce precisely foreseeable reactions. Such interference is even more dangerous than psychosurgery, because it needs neither direct surgical invasion nor destruction of tissue and can be given without the recipient's knowledge.

In the 1950s, drugs, such as chlorpromazine, isoniazid and imipramine, which were effective in dealing with mood phases, began to be used. These drugs enabled patients, once so utterly depressed or deluded that they had to be confined in hospitals, to return to active lives in the community. Various new major tranquillizers – Melleril, Stelazine, Serenace and others – made their appearance in quick succession, and have provided relief for patients with severe psychiatric conditions. Unfortunately, these drugs may also be used for nontherapeutic purposes, for example, in interrogation.

In 1848, Phineas P. Gage, twenty-five years old and vigorous in mind and body, was preparing a hole for blasting, in the course of railway construction. When he was tamping it with an iron, the powder exploded, driving the iron through his left cheek and out at the top of his head. Gage survived the accident, regaining consciousness in a few minutes. But it altered his character, and he became more capricious and childish. This shrewd, energetic man was so transformed that in the eyes of his friends he was 'no longer Gage'.[3] This incident, reported in the *Boston Medical and Surgical Journal*, was followed by studies of the effects on behaviour of lesions of the cerebral cortex in dogs and by pioneering human brain surgery by Sir Victor Horsley at University College Hospital, London.

At a 1935 Neurological Congress in London, two American scientists reported details of behaviour modification in chimpanzees as a result of destruction of prefrontal areas of the brain. A Portuguese neurologist, Dr Egas Moniz, asked the congress why, if frustration could be eliminated in animals, it was not possible to relieve anxiety in people by surgery. In Portugal, he put this idea into practice by operating on psychiatric patients who had failed to respond to other forms of treatment. He devised a technique of cutting brain fibres with a special knife which was inserted through an opening drilled in the skull, thus initiating lobotomies.

Since Moniz's operations, which won him a Nobel Prize, psychosurgery has gone through many phases. Walter Freeman and James Watts, Moniz's enthusiastic followers, pioneered new techniques and, before the procedures fell into disfavour, an estimated 50,000 prefrontal lobotomies were carried out in North America and 10,000 in Great Britain.[4]

Following these developments in psychosurgery, it was possible for scientists to locate the bundles of nerve centres or neurons which controlled particular kinds of conduct. And later it was possible, without massive surgery, to burn or destroy selected groups of neurons by introducing delicate electrical devices into the brain.

Psychosurgery began to look ominous when possibilities appeared of using it to quieten violent people. Vernon Mark and Frank Ervin, two neurosurgeons, described in *Violence and the Brain* the surgical procedures by which they had controlled violent behaviour. The implications of brain surgery as an aid to law and order were not lost in the context of the urban violence of the 1960s.

The spread of psychosurgery caused alarm. Some states, such as Oregon, banned it in 1973 as a threat to public health. The Oregon statute defined psychosurgery as any procedure that destroys brain tissue for the primary purpose of modifying behaviour. This description included operations which are now referred to as lobotomy, psychiatric surgery, and behavioural surgery, but excluded surgery for the removal of tumours and abscesses and the treatment of brain damage caused by accidents. The cutting of a portion of the frontal lobe is still a valid procedure for killing pain, and even in its most 'barbarous' days, up to 1955, psychosurgery was the last therapeutic resort for many psychiatric patients.[5]

With increasing improvements in psychosurgery, the type of control possible will be progressively refined, and it may be possible for the margin between therapeutic use and use for social control to be deliberately obscured. 'Deviant' conduct may include violence, alcoholism, homosexuality, drug addiction, argumentativeness, and political dissent.

The question who will determine whether a person is to be subjected to psychosurgery is more complex than in traditional medical or surgical treatment. By the very nature of the conditions for which the treatment is used, patients are often incapable of giving their consent.

Who then consents on behalf of the patient? What mandate does such a person have? What assurance of impartiality can there be when the 'patient' is already an inmate of a state institution: a prison, or infirmary or mental home? How can the law protect a person from being subjected to 'treatment' in order to produce a particular behavioural pattern? Free will, the cornerstone of all concepts of freedom under the law, stands undermined.

The question of bringing psychosurgery and all forms of brain manipulation under greater control is a difficult one. The critics of brain surgery have been attacked as being uninformed; the enthusiasts for continued research are under fire for their insufficient humanitarian concern. These modern surgical techniques give a new dimension to the ability to manipulate human behaviour.

As a result of the protest sparked off in the early days of psychosurgery, there have been several detailed studies of the manner in which controls can be applied. Among the better known are the report of the New South Wales Committee of Inquiry into Psychosurgery (1977) and the Report on Psychosurgery of the US National Commission for the Protection of Human Subjects of Biomedical and Behavioural Research (1977).

The New South Wales report suggests that all cases should be assessed by a psychosurgery review board comprising seven members including a lawyer, a psychologist, two psychiatrists, a neurosurgeon, and a representative of the public. Where there is doubt about the competence of a patient to give consent, there should be a reference to a Justice of the Supreme Court for a ruling.

The US report stresses that psychosurgery should not be used for any purpose other than to give treatment to individual patients. In particular, there is a prohibition on psychosurgery being performed on a prisoner, a patient involuntarily committed to a mental hospital and a patient believed to be incapable of giving informed consent, subject to certain exceptions. Psychosurgery should, according to the report, be performed only at an institution with an approved review board and by a competent surgeon, on a properly assessed, informed and consenting patient.

Particularly difficult questions arise where a patient in need of psychosurgery is in a prison and the medical officer in charge of the patient is a prison employee. To deal with the conflict of loyalties, he or she needs guidelines from the medical profession. Guidelines issued by the World Medical Association and by the United Nations Congress on the Prevention of Crime and the Treatment of Offenders, 1958, however, have not worked with much success.[6]

Some doctors believe that attempts at setting up external machinery for surveillance and control are a slur on the medical profession. The New South Wales recommendations, for example, were attacked by a contributor to the *Medical Journal of Australia*[7] as a 'near-libellous slur upon the medical profession'.

No such slur is intended by the proponents of machinery for the safeguard of individual rights, just as no slur is intended on scientists when it is argued that the public should participate in scientific decision making.

Article 6 of the World Psychiatric Association's Declaration of Hawaii suggests that whenever there is compulsory treatment or detention there must be an independent and neutral body of appeal for regular inquiry into these cases and that every patient must be informed of its existence.

In this area, it is difficult to accommodate the human rights of the patient, the needs of society and its institutions of confinement, the professional autonomy of the medical profession, and the concepts and procedures of the law.

Blanket condemnations are not the answer. We need a skilled and careful delineation of indications and methods. The current unregulated situation, however, denigrates people's rights. Only carefully thought out regulatory guidelines, based on adequate expertise, offer a solution. Now is the time to take stock.

Human Experimentation

In many areas of medicine, experimentation on humans is the surest means of furthering medical knowledge. But do the ends justify the means?

An incredulous world heard of appalling medical experiments on prisoners in concentration camps during World War II. In a letter to the commandant at Auschwitz, the chemical trust, I. G. Farben, wrote:

In contemplation of experiments with a new soporific drug, we would appreciate your procuring for us a number of women . . . We received your answer but consider the price of 200 marks a woman excessive. We propose to pay not more than 170 marks a head. If agreeable, we will take possession of the women. We need approximately 150 . . . Received the order of 150 women. Despite their emaciated condition, they were found satisfactory. We shall keep you posted on developments concerning this experiment . . . The tests were made. All subjects died. We shall contact you shortly on the subject of a new load.[8]

It is not only in wartime, however, that people's rights are violated. In August 1981, in the US, unsuspecting patients were subjected to experimental doses of high radiation in a government study for the space programme. The study centre, operated by the Atomic Energy Commission, routinely used radiation treatment of up to 500 rads over several hours on cancer patients who really became guinea pigs for the space programme.[9] A dose of 450 rads in one burst was enough to be fatal to half the people exposed. Another report[10] revealed that in 1980 the CIA had spent millions of dollars in drug experiments on people to control behaviour and sexual patterns, using private medical institutions and prominent universities for its secret programme.

Before the war, medical experimentation on humans was rarely the subject of study. Experiences in the war altered that, and, in 1946, the Nuremberg Code on Medical Experimentation appeared, listing ten basic principles. One of its cornerstones was that the subject of medical experiment should have sufficient knowledge and comprehension of the subject matter involved to enable an understanding and enlightened decision to be made.

The Nuremberg principles have been the subject of much further development. The World Medical Association elaborated these principles in its 1964 Declaration of Helsinki, which in turn was amended at Tokyo in 1975. Item 5 of the Helsinki Declaration enumerated the principle that concern for the interests of the subject must always prevail over the interests of science and society. Concern over a few notorious cases in the US led Congress to enact *The National Research Act* in 1974, creating a National Commission for the Protection of Human Subjects of Biomedical and Behavioural Research, which was given a mandate to identify basic ethical principles and to evolve guidelines. In 1982, the World Health Organization and the Council for International Organizations of Medical Sciences published a set of proposed international guidelines for bio-medical research. In the same year, the Australian National Health and Medical Research Council published a statement on human experimentation.

Experimentation on human beings for the advancement of medical knowledge is often carried out in universities and similar institutions which are committed to disinterested research and intensely conscious of the human rights implications of their work.

The free consent of the subject is essential before research is undertaken, but this proposition is easier to state than to apply. In many cases, especially in hospitals, the patient or subject is unable to decide for himself or herself, and the legal guardian is scarcely a substitute. In deciding whether to proceed with the research, the benefits to society and the inconvenience and discomfort of the patient must be balanced.

Testing New Drugs

In 1975, Dr William Sargant, one of Britain's best known and most respected senior psychiatrists, felt so disturbed by current clinical trials of drugs that he spoke of tests being carried out on 'large groups of . . . mentally tortured patients, so as to convince not those at the bedside who can soon see for themselves whether this drug is working, but laboratory statisticians and armchair writers who have generally been the reactionary critics in the advancing treatment scene . . .' [11]

Dr Sargant emphasized the need for the 'controlled' testing of drugs to be brought to the public's notice and for the rights of the patients and the ethical issues involved to be openly discussed. Experiments with drugs involve not only doctors but also pharmaceutical companies, industrial enterprises, military and prison authorities, and other government instrumentalities.

A distinction needs to be drawn between treatments undertaken as part of the possible cure of a sick person and procedures undertaken on healthy people for the advancement of scientific knowledge. A person should not be asked to sign away the right to compensation for damage as a result of the experiment. Aftercare should also be the responsibility of the experimenter.

A frequent method of testing drugs is through controlled trials. In a controlled trial, a proposed new treatment is compared with either no treatment or some established treatment. For this purpose, patients are divided into two or more groups, some being treated with the experimental procedure and others with a placebo. For the placebo to work, the patient cannot know to which treatment he or she is being subjected. The need for a person's consent and understanding tends to rule out placebo treatment in controlled groups, seriously impedes research, and raises a moral dilemma to which the answer, from the patient's point of view, seems to be that such procedures are not permissible.

The researcher must be acutely aware of his or her ethical obligations, because it is difficult to police such work. The danger is greatest in institutions of confinement where patients may be subtly coerced into participating in the research for fear of displeasing those in power.

In a more simple situation, where a patient is asked by his physician or surgeon for permission to be used in an experiment, the patient may feel such an obligation to or a dependence on the doctor as to be unable to withhold his or her consent, although theoretically free to do so. A patient requested to permit a blood sample to be taken for medical research, for example, may fear the consequences of displeasing the doctor whom he or she believes is the bridge between illness and good health.

Informed consent is especially difficult to obtain in the case of psychiatric treatment, where the patient is unable to take a balanced view.

The requirement of consent in medical treatment has assumed great importance in recent years in the context of actions for damages against doctors. The fear of litigation arising from an allegation that the patient did not know the nature of the treatment to which he or she was to be subjected has triggered off a change of attitude, and it may be that this factor rather than the medico-ethical one has been the inducement for explaining to patients the after-effects of treatment.

These are some guidelines, the implementation of which is essential to the preservation of the rights of people subjected to medical experiments.

● The subject should be fully informed of the purpose of the trial, and of the risks and benefits.

● Rewards offered for participation should not be such as to persuade the subject to take unreasonable risks.

● All costs and expenses of the subject should be met by the experimenter.

● The experimentation should be in the hands of competent people, and laboratory and animal experiments should have preceded its trial on humans.

● Experiments should not to be undertaken in the absence of provision for long-term care and observation.

● Legal arrangements should be made for compensating the subject if long-term health problems arise as a result of the experiment.

● The investigator should not be absolved from liability.

● The safety of the subject should take priority over the success of the experiment.

● A patient's bill of rights needs to be proclaimed.

● Subjects should be chosen because they are appropriate for the experiment rather than because they happen to be available.

● Consent may at any time be withdrawn.

● Committees should be set up to supervise all aspects of the research, and doctors and patients should be told the implications for human rights of the experimental techniques being used.[12]

● The patient's identity must be kept confidential.

The idea of a patients' bill of rights is neither new nor fanciful. It was mooted and promulgated by the American Hospitals Association over ten years ago. Such a bill of rights gives both patients and doctors a clear indication of their rights and duties. It would cover such areas as experimentation, privacy and confidentiality, the duty of care, consent to treatment, diagnostic tests, and malpractice. World Health Organization committees have been working in this area, and the national legal systems need to pay attention to the international standards thus evolving.

At the same time, an educational programme, bringing the medical profession the latest developments in this field, is needed. Campaigns to educate the public about their rights as patients would be useful, just as campaigns were mounted by legal authorities to acquaint people with their basic legal rights.

The Right to Die

The extraordinary medical procedures we have looked at in the context of mind manipulation and medical experimentation are only two instances of the ethical problems such procedures create. More poignant than these are the issues raised by extraordinary medical procedures used on the terminally ill.

Judge Cooley, in a treatise on the law of torts, observed that every human being has 'the right to be let alone'. The right to be let alone includes in the view of some commentators not only the right to live but also the right to die.

For these reasons, right to die movements have been pressing for voluntary euthanasia in the case of the seriously ill, the incapacitated and the dying, and societies have come into existence such as Exit, a British society for the right to die with dignity.

Sophisticated life support apparatus, often needed for the support of more viable lives, cannot be used indefinitely, and modern medicine's ability to keep the heart beating or the lungs breathing, while there is no other hope of recovery, places on the relatives the agony of watching an apparently painful and prolonged death. It also places on the state a burden of heavy expenditure. These are some of the questions that arise:

● When is it justifiable to withdraw life support systems?
● Is the cost to the community of maintaining sophisticated life support apparatus relevant in the decision to withdraw it?
● Is there a right to die in the sense that a person ought to be able to decide whether he or she will opt to continue treatment?
● If there is such a right, how does one draw a distinction between cases where its exercise is permissible and impermissible?
● Is there a danger that those with an interest in succession to the estate of the patient may for selfish reasons request the withdrawal of life support systems?
● In communities short of medical resources, is there justification for keeping a hospital bed occupied indefinitely by an incurable and unconscious individual?
● To whom should the decision to withdraw life support be entrusted?

Passive euthanasia or the inducement of gentle death by the non-use or withdrawal of treatment necessary to sustain life has been reported to be widely practised by Australian and foreign doctors and, on 20 November 1975, the chief of the Royal Melbourne Hospital Intensive Care Unit was reported in the Melbourne *Herald* to have said: 'It is widespread normal medical procedure to disconnect artificial support systems keeping hopeless patients just alive. I have done it myself. It is part of the normal medical procedure.'

Many doctors were reluctant, however, to practise passive euthanasia, fearing that charges of neglect or even prosecution could follow such action, under present laws.

The Karen Quinlan case in the US brought these issues to the public notice in 1976 when the parents of a girl who had been reduced to a vegetable state by severe brain damage sought permission to have her respirator switched off. Her physician had refused the parents' request on the grounds that the proposed action would be contrary to medical practice and ethics. Lawyers for five parties opposed the parents, arguing that death as a result of the removal of the respirator would be murder. The appeal court allowed the parents' application. They observed that the parents were requesting authorization for no more than what medical authorities had been practising in the past without express authorization by law. They made clear at the same time that they were not leaving an opening for active euthanasia.

The Quinlan case resulted in legislation in a number of states to permit an adult of sound mind to declare that 'extraordinary life sustaining procedures' should be withdrawn once he or she had met certain conditions. This type of document is known as a 'living will', and gives effect to the human right to die a natural death. The State of California has enacted a *Natural Death Act*, the first in the common law world permitting an adult to execute a 'directive' to a physician to withdraw life-support systems in prescribed circumstances.

Australia has produced drafts of similar legislation: a Natural Death Bill was introduced in South Australia in 1980, for example, and reported on by a Select Committee of the Legislative Council. The medical witnesses who gave evidence before the Select Committee took the view initially that current medical practice was satisfactory and that there was little need for legislation. Later, however, they conceded that patients could have reasonable fears that they would be subjected to excessive technological efforts to prolong their lives. The committee urged the reintroduction of the bill to allow adults who did not wish to be subjected to extraordinary measures to keep them alive if they were suffering a terminal illness to issue an instruction which would be legally binding on those treating them.

> *Thou shalt not kill; but needst not strive*
> *Officiously to keep alive*

expresses one form of resolution of the ethical dilemma involved. Gallup polls are being used in various countries to sound out public opinion. In Australia, for example, a Gallup poll showed that 72 per cent of the public were in favour of positive euthanasia where a patient suffering from an incurable and distressing illness wished to end his or her life.[13]

The power of modern medicine to postpone death produces a conflict between two moral obligations of the medical profession: to relieve suffering and to extend life. There was a time when these were synonymous. Today, many elderly patients, who would but for medical advances have died naturally, are now rescued from death but maintained artificially with painful and incurable illnesses or in 'vegetable' conditions.

Doctors' guilt, if they feel they have failed to do all that is humanly possible to extend life, may complicate their medical decisions. The distinction between treating and neglecting patients often turns out to be a semantic one on which no adequate guidelines have been laid down.

Guidelines become important when you realize that doctors themselves have an impermissibly wide range of views on their duties and their patients' rights on the question of euthanasia.

In a study of decision making in critical illness,[14] a New South Wales researcher examined doctors' reactions to terminally ill patients. The doctors were asked, 'What do doctors generally do when a decision has to be made about prolonging or terminating a life?' Of fifty-four specialists and thirty-four general practitioners asked, twenty and eighteen respectively were of the view that it becomes obvious when you should stop. Seven doctors in each group thought they should be helped to die, seventeen doctors of the first group and eight of the second group thought that life should be kept going as long as possible. Clearly, medical ethics has been unable to work out a uniform response to this question, and doctors can hold and act on opposing views. Some doctors defined withholding blood or antibiotics as being a moral decision but refusing to give treatment as a technical decision which was clearly within their competence.

Perhaps because the code which doctors learn does not include morality and philosophy, they do not perceive that both are moral decisions as well as technical ones.[15]

When the researcher in this study probed the manner of decision making, she found that some doctors (six out of thirty) thought that there was no need to make decisions. Others decided after consulting relatives and patients (ten out of thirty). Some thought there was no need for decisions if one always tried to save the patient (six out of thirty), and some resorted to discussions with their colleagues (eight out of thirty). Some doctors responded to the question, 'How do you help a patient cope with news of a terminal illness?' by saying that the question was irrelevant to them.

It is not only the aged or terminally ill who present these problems. Many young adults are accident victims or suffer from illnesses such as kidney disease. Although not terminally ill, they may prefer to die, requesting their doctors to withhold treatment. The ethical duties of doctors in this situation are not yet the subject of any guidelines. As medicine progresses, the period of incapacitation will be prolonged, thus forcing the issue sooner or later on the courts.

Similar issues have arisen in the context of religious objections to medical treatment, as where a Jehovah's Witness refuses an essential blood transfusion. The right to refuse treatment in these circumstances has been upheld in some US decisions even when death would inevitably follow; others have held that patients' wishes should be overridden as the patient has no constitutional 'right to die'.[16]

On 6 July 1979, the *Canberra Times* reported the case of Elizabeth Burgers, a Jehovah's Witness, who died in hospital after refusing a blood transfusion on religious grounds. She was told she needed the transfusion but refused. A hospital spokesman said, 'Had she been a minor we could have forced her to have a transfusion. But had we gone ahead without her permission we could have faced charges of assault.'

Babies that are grossly deformed at birth present similar issues. Diseases such as Down's syndrome, cerebral palsy and spina bifida condemn their sufferers to a life of prolonged misery. There is evidence that some doctors withhold treatment from such children and that others treat them just as they would treat normal children. Here again the absence of guidelines results in varying attitudes and in an unfortunate divergence between what doctors are actually doing and what they are professing to do. What happens, then, is often the result of chance rather than of any considered medical or legal directives.

Community attitudes towards the grossly deformed child have varied. The Athenians killed deformed children. The Roman Emperor Justinian in his *Digest*, which is the source of much European law, denied basic rights to a child so grossly deformed as not to be in human form. Modern community attitudes are changing with medicine's ability to identify an increasing number of diseases prenatally, such as Down's syndrome and spina bifida.

The question of the withholding of medical treatment is complicated further by medical advances which can keep a body pulsating when all brain and nervous activity have permanently ceased. Should such a person be kept 'alive'? To answer the question, we must know whether such a person is legally dead. But what is the test of legal death?

We have become aware that there are different kinds of death: physiological death, when vital activities have ceased, intellectual death, when brain function is permanently halted, and neurological death, when the nervous system ceases to function. We are not talking here of other notions of death such as spiritual and social death.

But neither religion nor ethics can offer definitive guidelines on when or where death occurs. In 1957, Pope Pius XII observed, for example, that the soul may have already left the body where vital functions are maintained by extraordinary means over a prolonged period in a deeply unconscious individual.[17]

What would the situation be in a hypothetical case where various tissues or organs of the body are kept alive after a person's death? If substantial portions of the body can be kept alive despite death, we will be forced to identify that part of the body which is essential to life. We tend to be reduced to two or three principal organs: the heart, the brain, and possibly the lungs. Although the continuing functioning of any one of these can be used as an index of bodily life, no one of them is an exclusive indicator. Already we pronounce a person dead whose heart keeps on beating in another's body.

Some arbitrary choices need to be made, an example of which is the Australian Law Reform Commission's decision to include irreversible loss of brain function in its definition of death.[18] The commission has also recommended that the specific tests for establishing brain death should be left to the medical profession. As a result of its recommendations the Australian Capital Territory Ordinance No. 44 of 1978 reads:

For the purposes of the law of the Territory a person has died when there has occurred
(a) irreversible cessation of all function of the brain of a person; or
(b) irreversible cessation of circulation of blood in the body of the person.

Other Australian states have followed this recommendation, but in Britain there was violent opposition to this notion. After the controversy provoked by a BBC 'Panorama' programme in 1980, it was suggested that brain death be more clearly identified by performing an electroencephalogram (a record of the electrical activity of the brain). The decision on brain death may involve more than a dozen different criteria and may be viewed differently by different doctors. Whether such stringent requirements are necessary is a matter for informed community decision, but one observable effect of such an approach is to reduce greatly the number of organs available for transplantation. It is thought that the halving of kidney transplant operations in Britain following the BBC

'Panorama' programme was the result of a consequently lower number of available donors.[19]

The question when death occurs is no longer an academic one but one given practical significance by organ transplant techniques and life support apparatus. Organ transplants raise the question in view of the importance of ascertaining that death has occurred before a vital organ is removed. Instances are on record of people who have been certified dead reviving in mortuaries or on operating tables, as in the case of Mrs Roseberry in the US,[20] who revived just before she was embalmed, the Birmingham case, where an operation to remove kidneys was in progress when signs of life were noticed and the operation stopped,[21] or the Melbourne case, where a body walked out of the Morgue and was found wandering around naked in the cold.[22]

The problem of the 'right to die' thus bristles with difficulties involving ethical, theological, and economic issues, in addition to those concerning medicine, law, and human rights. We have referred to only some. Many more will keep surfacing as medical science progresses. Definitive answers are not easily forthcoming, and in some cases may never emerge owing to the fundamental nature of the value judgments involved. Our understanding of the issues is as yet comparatively undeveloped, and it is only by fuller discussion that their many nuances will be comprehended. Such understanding will not emerge without a maximum exposure of these issues to public discussion and debate.

Medical Confidentiality

A particular aspect of patients' rights which has attracted special attention in the debate on privacy is the question of medical confidentiality. The Australian Law Reform Commission has done much to heighten the public's consciousness in this area. Genetic and personal information recorded for medical purposes will often be recorded by computer, and many of the issues relating to protection of computerized information will be relevant here. It is essential in cases of artificial insemination or tissue transplant that both donor and donee be protected, but that the relevant information should be available when required for medical purposes. Privacy law must take this within its ambit.

Different legal systems have different rules on this matter. The Australian Law Reform Commission, in its 1977 working paper on tissue transplants, draws attention to the need for privacy in a national register of donors. The Canadian *Uniform Act on Transplantation* proscribes the identification of possible donors and recipients. The South African act forbids disclosure of identity without the person's consent. The Australian Law Reform Commission recommended that disclosure of personal information should be forbidden except with the person's consent.

Difficult issues arise in various fields. Elaborate information about the donor's physical and medical history, and his family medical background, for example, will be essential to a sperm bank and to doctors for a pregnancy by artificial insemination by a donor. From the social point of view, however, protecting the donor's identity is crucial. To what extent this secrecy can be preserved on a life-long basis, especially where sperm banks are commercialized (and the information computerized) is a difficult practical question. In the event of litigation, for example, in an action brought by a child for having wrongfully been brought into life, the court would need to have access to all details, and presumably this information would become available to the lawyers on both sides. If the donor's identity is still to be kept secret, the court's power may need to be circumscribed by legislation. The common law is inadequate to deal with this situation.

The conflict between individual privacy and the social benefits of medical research was the subject of discussion at a Council of Europe conference held in Belgium in September 1980. It was recognized there that although medical research is important, it is not the predominant interest.[23] The person who is the subject of medical research is entitled to privacy on symptoms, diagnosis, treatment and after effects. Psychiatry is a particularly sensitive area, as the American Psychiatric Association recognized at its Bellagio conference in August 1977, when it highlighted the importance of patient consent as a prerequisite to data collection.

Some people have argued that some loss of freedom is the price one pays for the benefits one draws from society.[24] If this statement is examined in the light of psychiatric and contraceptive treatment, or in the context of diseases, such as epilepsy and heart malfunction, which carry a social stigma, a person's privacy is clearly more important than the general advancement of medical knowledge.

The increasing powers of search and seizure given to the police and the department of health and consumer protection services threaten to break down our right to confidentiality in medical treatment. These new powers were the subject of numerous complaints to the Australian Law Reform Commission in November 1980. In New South Wales, a proposal to amend the *Consumer Protection Act* to enable officers of the Consumer Affairs Department to seize and examine confidential patient records caused a public outcry in January 1981.[25] Further, an increasing number of migrants in various countries have their medical records kept in a language which they do not comprehend, and even if they had the right to inspect their files, they would not be able to understand the information recorded. This is most dangerous in psychiatry.

These are the main questions that arise in this area:

● How is the conflict resolved between the needs of medical research and the privacy of patients?

● How are patients to be assured that they will have access to their medical records?

● Are there instances in which patients should be denied access to their records?

● How is secrecy to be maintained on donor's and recipient's identity in sperm banks?

● Should information be available on a donor's identity in the case of storage or donation of organs?

● Should parents have the right to see their children's medical records?

● What are children's rights to confidentiality about their medical conditions?

● What safeguards need to be implemented to protect people against the police, and medical and other authorities gaining access to their medical records?

● What guidelines can be offered to courts faced with a disputed claim of confidentiality?
● Should patients who are not parties in a case have a right to be informed that their medical records will be produced?
● Are there any special areas of medical records, for example, psychiatric illness, venereal disease, pregnancy, which need special protection?

Organs and Tissue
Organ Transplants

The legal issues raised by organ transplants attracted world-wide prominence in December 1967 when Dr Christian Barnard in South Africa performed the first heart transplant operation.

Apart from the human brain, which presents transplant problems at present considered beyond the reach of science, many other vital organs seem to be capable of transplantation. Steady progress has been made in the field of countering the host bodies' rejection mechanisms.

Skin grafts were performed 2,000 years ago in India. Since then bones, blood, blood vessels, corneas, teeth, ear tissue, kidneys, livers, lungs, cartilages, hearts, and pituitary glands have all been used in transplant surgery, successful or otherwise.

Organ transplants raise questions about property in the human body, the sale of organs, the maintenance of organ banks, the priorities to be observed when there are many applicants for a limited number of organs, the principles for determining whether death has occurred before an organ may be removed for transplantation, the right of a donor to grant permission for the removal of an organ from his or her body while still alive, the legal liability of medical staff who use organs from a body which may not be clinically dead, and the circumstances in which an organ may be removed from a child to save the life of another, as, for example, when a kidney is removed from one twin to save the life of the other. The common law has not yet provided answers to these questions.

The human body, sacrosanct according to Christian teaching, is not a piece of property, not even the 'owner's'. It cannot be sold.

The same considerations apply to parts of the human body. A private organization cannot 'sell' organs or body parts, and if a bank of these were maintained, it could only be done so by a state authority.

Medical advances in storing organs which have been removed from dead bodies make it possible for vast numbers of organs to be taken out of dead bodies and stored. The state may have an interest in securing the maximum number of organs, especially where they are difficult to match, and storing them for future use. In the circumstances, should people have the right to withhold the use of their bodies after death? If they refuse to permit their organs or bodies to be stored after their death, can the state override their wishes? If people do not specifically object, must they be taken to have consented?

In some cases, it is inadequate to remove an organ from a dead body. In kidney, heart and liver transplantation, removal must be from a living body, or from a body in a condition as near to living as possible. Questions of consent arise. Often the living body which is the only available source may be the body of a child, perhaps an identical twin. Bone marrow, which will be regenerated in the body of the donor, may be urgently required to save a life. Who can give consent in such cases – parent, guardian, court, hospital committee or state?

Here there may be a conflict of interests between the rights of the dead and the rights of the dying. Consider the case of Bill Mathews in the US who, being thought dead through cessation of brain function, was being prepared for an operation to remove his heart, when a chance movement of his Adam's apple gave the surgeon second thoughts about proceeding. Spared, he lived to lead an active life.

Physicians or surgeons performing transplant operations may also find themselves in conflict. Acting for patients needing the donation, and paid by them, they may not be in the best position to make the decisions whether organs should be removed from people who are apparently dead. Irreversible brain damage may be a test of clinical death, as the Australian Law Reform Commission has suggested, but this may be difficult to decide with certainty in the absence of a reading on an encephalograph of the electrical activities of the brain.

Among relatives there will be people who may be influenced, consciously or unconsciously, by the advantages they may derive from their relation's death. If the decision to donate body tissue from a seriously injured person depends on such an interested party, there is always the possibility that this power will be abused, under cover of concern for the patient. Likewise, physicians employed by them may be influenced to shut off life-support systems. In the expressive words of a former Australian governor-general, Sir Zelman Cowen, who has for many years interested himself academically in these questions: 'When a doctor really wants an organ from a dying man, then I simply cannot have 100 per cent confidence that there will be a 100 per cent effort to keep him from dying.'[26]

It is difficult to police rules about the removal of organs from dead bodies without consent when it is easy to remove them without disfiguring the body, as in the case of the pituitary gland, the hormones from which are used to treat infertility and retarded growth.

Whether it is desirable to allocate scarce community resources for the expensive technology involved in transplants is another question. When the 'immune response' (that is, the rejection of foreign tissue by the human body) can be overcome, hormone producing glands – the pituitary, thyroid, parathyroid, adrenal, testes and ovary – will be capable of being successfully transplanted.[27] Already, new anti-rejection drugs, such as Cyclosporin-A, have been developed, and immunological research is progressing rapidly.

It is not difficult to predict the complex legal problems that will arise if and when the testes and ovary can be transplanted. Quite apart from the problems associated with obtaining such glands (certification of death, consent, and so on), lawyers will be concerned with claims about legitimacy, parentage, inheritance and maintenance, and actions for wrongful birth.

The Royal College of Obstetricians and Gynaecologists

Australian Council, in a submission to the Australian Law Reform Commission, said that the transplantations of Fallopian tubes and ovaries, though not yet successfully made, are regarded as definite future possibilities, and will be in demand by infertile women.

There have recently been attempts by Stanford University's pioneering transplant team at simultaneous transplantations of the heart and lungs in rhesus monkeys. Lung transplants in humans have not yet been successful, and no recipients have survived longer than ten months. In humans, the few attempts that have been made at combined heart-lung transplants have failed.

Clear guidelines must be drawn up on the certification of death and the removability of organs. The Australian Law Reform Commission's recommendation of certification of death by two independent doctors and of the use of cessation of brain function as a test of death is one solution.

The French decision that organs belong to the state after death unless a person has specified otherwise is one answer to the second problem.

Enzyme Engineering

We are coming steadily closer to imitating the complex chemical and engineering processes in the living cell. These processes are governed by protein catalysts called enzymes, and scientists are using sophisticated engineering techniques to use these enzymes in medical treatment. By this means, the presence of urea in the blood, which results from kidney malfunction, can be reduced.[28] The technology of fabricating porous membranes has also reached the point where pore sizes can be accurately controlled.

These procedures open up the possibility of manufacturing artificial organs which mimic natural membranes and in doing so raise another set of ethical questions.[29] These organs may be externally operated, as artificial kidneys are operated, or implanted in the patient, like an artificial heart.

Once these techniques become established, they can improve in certain respects on the performance of natural organs.

It may be that in the future these artificial organs will be used externally, mainly owing to the threat of rejection, but implantation is also a possibility and has been successful in animals. Either way, it will be difficult to determine the order and priority of donees where the artificial organ is expensive and patients requiring them exceed the supply.

Some of the issues raised by enzyme engineering are these:
- Just as the technology is developing for synthesizing drugs, such as non-immunogenic biocatalysts, the same technology can be used for breeding new kinds of chemical weapons.
- The increased dependence on laboratory facilities could lead to the depersonalization of the doctor-patient relationship.
- The delaying of death, once artificial organs become easily available, may result in new social problems of ageing populations.
- The trend towards expensive therapeutic technology could increase government control over many areas of treatment.
- A dichotomy could become increasingly evident between the doctor's role as protector of the patient's individual rights and a new role as guardian of expensive community equipment.

Sale and Hire of Human Organs and Tissue
Legal writers are already discussing the possibility of human organ banks trading with poorer countries.[30] A kidney, for example, could be bought from a poor donor in the Third World for a few thousand dollars, which would make him or her affluent. Donees in the west would be happy to pay thousands of dollars to receive an organ that would enable him or her to live a full life.

If this becomes acceptable, the poorer countries will be seen as rich reservoirs of human organs. To many, this erodes the concept of human dignity and the sanctity of the human body. Such a traffic, however, might be difficult to detect. International laws will need to back up national laws to try to stamp out the trade.

New developments in genetic medicine add other dimensions to the problem. Artificial insemination procedures make surrogate motherhood possible. Fees of $10,000 have already been paid to surrogate mothers in the US. A woman may also rent her uterus for more altruistic reasons, such as helping a sister or a friend who is unable for medical reasons to carry her own baby. If such procedures are permitted, should unmarried women be allowed to do it, and should married women require their husbands' consent?

If there is a contract, what would the position be if the natural mother wanted the surrogate to have an abortion against her wish? What legal remedies would the foetus have against either mother in the event of damage through defective medical procedures? Would the natural mother have claims against the surrogate mother if the foetus is damaged through her negligence? Once such a contract has been entered into, can it be legally enforced? Do different principles apply to the hire of body parts from those for their sale? In the US, 'womb-renting' is now done by mail-order contracts. Commercial mail-ordering services bring the contracting parties together for implantation. In the absence of statute law, precedent, and ethical guidelines, however, the whole field is open. The legal issue arises from the value placed on motherhood in the law. Mothers' rights are recognized by many legal systems as paramount, and they often prevail, despite the responsibilities of mothers where marriages break up. Surrogate motherhood confronts the law with the unprecedented situation of two mothers: one who donates the ovum and the other who nurtures the child. Can the rights of the surrogate mother be contracted away for a financial payment (currently ranging from $10,000 to $20,000)? What is the effect on the law of adoption? Does the surrogate mother who changes her mind and wants to retain the child she has borne have the right to resile from the contract and surrender the child to its natural parents? Can any guidelines be laid down for the selection of surrogates?

Indeed, some members of the legal profession may enter this field and provide services for arranging surrogate births, just as lawyers' offices are sometimes used to settle deals between buyers and sellers in land transactions.

It is anticipated that there will be a number of cases in the US shortly which ask for a decision on the legality and the consequences of contracts for surrogate mothers. Confusion could arise if different state jurisdictions take different views. A couple in one state, for example, may hire a surrogate mother in another as has already happened. An Illinois couple hired a surrogate mother in Kentucky, raising the possibility that the Kentucky attorney-general could institute a law suit on the basis that the transaction was illegal.[31]

The matter is of special importance because it involves the transfer of a child from one state jurisdiction to another. The problem can assume international significance if surrogate mothers are hired from a developing country. Questions of citizenship of the child and the legality of his or her transfer across international borders will then arise.

Contracts for surrogate motherhood will be resorted to not only by couples who are childless but also by single people, such as lesbians and homosexuals, thus raising further problems of the extent of control to be exercised over such procedures.

It is likely that there will be a large number of surrogate mothers in the future, considering that in a country with a small population, such as Australia, it is estimated that there are 40,000 infertile couples. Already offers have been made to the in vitro fertilization programme at Monash University from women who, through surrogate motherhood, wish to help couples who are unable to have their own children. A New South Wales couple is reported to have offered $10,000 for a suitable surrogate mother and there have been many responses.[32] The ethics committee which guides the programme at Monash University has adopted the position that the legal questions surrounding surrogate motherhood should first be settled before any offers are accepted.

Among questions to be sorted out initially, apart from the legality of the contract, are the listing of parents' names on the birth certificate, inheritance, and the competing claims of the natural and surrogate mothers. In a recent US case, a surrogate mother refused to surrender the child to the parents, and it was discovered minutes before the case was heard in Pasadena that the mother seeking custody of the child had been through a sex change operation five years earlier. The case was dropped in view of the publicity it would arouse which would prevent the child leading a normal life. The case also involved the legal systems of New York and California as the evidence was that the frozen sperm was flown from New York, where the couple lived, to California, where it was used to impregnate the surrogate mother. The first judicial acceptance of a surrogate motherhood contract occurred in San Francisco on 26 April 1981, when the court ruled that the father and his wife could claim legal parenthood from the surrogate mother by proceedings which were similar to adoption proceedings.

Not only human organs but human tissue can become the subject of commerce. Section 44 E(1)(f) of the federal *Medical (Organ Transplants) Act* makes it an offence to use 'for purposes other than therapeutic purposes any part removed from the body of a deceased person, or any therapeutic substance produced therefrom . . .' This provision was invoked in August 1981 by the Acting Victorian Health Minister in the context of the preparation and sale of humatrol, a quality control serum used to check the accuracy of testing systems in pathology laboratories. The Commonwealth Serum Laboratories had obtained the human tissue for the preparation of this first all-human product from the Royal Melbourne Hospital, which stated that about 15 cubic centimetres of pancreas had been removed from a cadaver, with the relatives' permission, and had been supplied to the serum laboratory. The Health Commission directed the Royal Melbourne Hospital to stop supplying the tissue until the legal position was clarified.

Another source of human tissue is the pituitary gland. This gland, removed from the brain, frozen and thereafter processed into powdery form, is the base of an injection which helps physically retarded children to resume normal growth. Present procedures for obtaining it can scarcely be described as legal, for during an autopsy the pituitary gland is often removed without permission or authority. The Commonwealth Serum Laboratory in Australia obtains about 12,000 pituitary glands a year. Procedures need to be established so that this substance may be legally obtained and its marketing and availability regulated.

Blood is big business, and the plasma industry is estimated to be worth between 200 and 250 million dollars a year in the US. Blood is bought and sold in some South American countries, such as El Salvador, and reputedly some individuals literally bleed themselves to death to keep their families above starvation level.

Foetal material is much sought after not only for experimental purposes but also for extracting from it tissue for therapeutic and cosmetic purposes. Such tissue is indispensable, for example, in cancer research, and it is possible that the pancreatic tissue (which produces insulin) of aborted babies may be transplanted in diabetics to give them a natural source of insulin.[33]

Birth and Procreation

Amniocentesis and Foetoscopy

Fundamental to our social organization is nature's approximation of an equal division of population between male and female. Over the centuries, and in all communities, this balance has been maintained, despite preferences that may exist in certain societies for male or female children, largely because of our inability to predict the sex of the child.

Amniocentesis and other techniques enable sex determination within sixteen weeks of conception. Research is progressing on techniques which even anticipate conception by separating male-producing sperm from female-producing sperm or by suppressing one or the other group or by rendering the female receptive to only one.

Given a marked preference for the one sex in a particular community, should a doctor reveal the sex of the foetus to a mother in the early weeks of pregnancy? Social pressures for a boy or a girl may be so strong as to result in a request for abortion. For this reason, current medical ethics do not favour revealing the sex to the mother, for this is neither diagnostic nor therapeutic information. In communities where abortion is or becomes permissible on demand, parents would theoretically be able to avoid a child of an undesired sex. When, in the foreseeable future, sex can be selected in anticipation of conception, there will be an even greater danger that the male-female ratio may be affected. In that event, all concepts of family law and social organization may change. The human rights of women (or of men) can be grievously damaged as the sex ratio alters. Legislation may be needed to restore the balance.

Knowledge of a child's sex in the early months of pregnancy is only a part of the increasing spectrum of information modern medical science is revealing about the foetus.

Amniocentesis, by which a specimen of the amniotic fluid withdrawn from the mother is analysed, permits a variety of diseases of the foetus to be diagnosed before birth. Foetoscopy, by which the foetus itself is invaded and a specimen of fluid withdrawn, allows the diagnosis of a wider range of foetal afflictions.

These procedures enable the mother and her doctor to know by the sixteenth week of pregnancy whether the child carries a disability, such as thalassaemia major, sickle cell anaemia, or spina bifida, for which no cure is known and which condemn the child and its family to a prolonged period of suffering.

Let us take one of these diseases, thalassaemia, and pursue the present medical advances in its diagnosis and treatment through their human rights implications.

Thalassaemia, a disease of the blood, which particularly afflicts people of Mediterranean and Asian origin, is caused by a haemoglobin defect.[34] Because of its prevalence among migrant communities in Australia, Australia has become the world's leading centre of thalassaemia research.

At present, the disease cannot be cured. The minor version of this disease (thalassaemia beta minor) can be endured without apparent ill effect, but in the virulent form (thalassaemia beta major), although a child may be born apparently healthy, it becomes pale and listless within the first year. The defective red blood cells the child produces are rapidly destroyed, and with increasing anaemia, owing to the body's attempt to produce more and more red blood cells, spleen and liver enlarge, skull and facial characteristics change and brittle bones cause pain.

Before modern medical treatment, a child with this disease rarely survived beyond five years, but constant blood transfusions could keep such a child alive, ten years ago, to the age of fifteen to twenty-five years, at which stage the iron overload in the system caused by constant transfusions caused degeneration of heart, kidneys, and liver. Today, treatment with desferrioxanin reduces the iron overload and enables people with this disease to survive until they are fifty or more. The treatment is very expensive, costing the community half a million dollars to keep each patient alive until the age of fifty.

A person suffering from thalassaemia minor marrying a person also suffering from the disease has a one in four chance of producing a child suffering from thalassaemia major, and foetoscopy enables physicians to predict by the sixth week of pregnancy whether the child to be born will have this defect.

Some other relevant factors are that the incidence of thalassaemia minor in some Mediterranean communities can be as high as 10 per cent, that the risk of foetoscopy to the foetus is around 5 per cent, that people who suffer from thalassaemia major appear to be happy and to value their lives, but that they put a great strain on their families, and that around 150 people who have thalassaemia major in a small state, such as Victoria, will cost the community about $75 million.

The issue to be determined is between the sanctity of life on the one hand and the cost to the community and the quality of life for the child and its family on the other. But other conflicts raised are those between maternal and foetal rights, between the tangible values of material resources and the intangible values of human integrity, between post-natal rights and pre-natal (and indeed pre-conceptual) rights, and between the backward glance of medical therapy and the forward perspectives of genetic counselling. These are some of the human rights issues raised by the use of foetoscopy in the diagnosis of thalassaemia:

● Does the danger to the foetus make foetoscopy unacceptable?

● Should a woman be informed that her routine blood sample is also being tested for thalassaemia?

● Should the mother be asked to give an undertaking before the test that if the foetus is found to be a thalassaemia major, she will consent to an abortion?

• Does the risk of diagnostic error stand in the way of the decision to abort?

• Is abortion of a foetus justified on the basis of a prenatal diagnosis of thalassaemia major?

• Who are entitled to make this decision: the mother, both parents, doctors, third parties, or a combination of these?

• How is the right to life of the foetus evaluated against the 'quality of life' of the parents, the 'quality of life' of the foetus, and the cost to the community of keeping it alive?

• What principles should be followed by genetic counsellors in advising a mother whose foetus is found to suffer from thalassaemia major?

• How is the hope of future advances in medicine relevant to the determination of abortion?

• Is the progressive deterioration of genetic stock resulting from the possibility of people with thalassaemia major procreating in the future to be counted as a factor favouring abortion?

• Should the entire community be screened for thalassaemia, or does one screen only pregnant women?

• Should there be a duty of disclosure before marriage that one is thalassaemic?

• Is it legitimate to require people suffering from thalassaemia major to undergo sterilization, or conceive only by artificial insemination by donor?

• Would the foetus, if not aborted, have a right of action against parent or physician or both for not having aborted it: the 'wrongful life' concept?

• Would the parents have an action for negligence in the performance and evaluation of the test, or defective counselling?

• What approach should one adopt to the clash of value systems between the counsellors and the patients, for example, Anglo-Saxon counsellors and Greek or Lebanese patients, and if so, what guidelines can we offer?

Thalassaemia is a useful illustration of some of the major issues. How important they are can be gathered from the realization that new Mendelian disorders are becoming capable of ante-natal detection at the rate of about one a week.[35] Other diseases such as spina bifida raise similar clusters of issues.

With the application of new molecular techniques to medical genetics, the loose collection in the 1970s of isolated pieces of genetic information have now transformed this area into systematic new sub-disciplines such as neurogenetics, immunogenetics, and behavioural genetics, each of them raising groups of human rights issues. One of the central and most difficult questions is, 'How defective is too defective?' The commonsense standards of the community are at best hazy guides, and there will be different standards among different cultural groups.

Just as different genetic sub-disciplines arose in the 1980s, so genetic counselling has become a recognized profession. The translation of the genetic information revealed by such techniques as amniocentesis and foetoscopy into terms which can be communicated sensitively to the patient has become a specialized task. Misinformation on a man's proneness to Huntingdon's chorea, a disease that afflicts middle-aged men, for example, has been known to result in suicide, and tactless information on the sex of embryos, without considering ethnic backgrounds, has resulted in needless abortions. Misdiagnosis is inherent in these pre-natal procedures, and the calculation of likely genetic defects demands expert care. False expectations can also be raised, for although pre-natal diagnostic procedures can detect a growing number of defects, there are many others, such as club feet or cleft palate, which will not be diagnosed.

An illustration of the ethical and counselling issues relating to probabilities is seen in the diagnosis of Down's syndrome by amniocentesis. The probability of a mother aged thirty-five having a child with Down's syndrome is one in 360. The risk of damage to the foetus by amniocentesis is one in a hundred. A mother aged thirty-five who has amniocentesis exposes her foetus to a risk of death four times as great as the risk that the child has Down's syndrome. If an action for negligence could arise from not using modern diagnostic procedures to warn of the defect, an action should also be able to be brought if there is no adequate warning of the risks of the procedure and for negligent counselling services. Clearly, expert counselling skills will be needed side by side with the new procedures.

Foetal tissue from aborted foetuses and from foetuses destined for abortion are used for experiments in genetic research. It may be that the unborn foetus does not yet have a legal personality, but modern scientific research shows unequivocally that the foetus has many characteristics of the human.

The question assumes great importance in the light of inflammatory reports of foetal abuse by scientists. It has been reported, for example, that living embryos have been sold by abortion clinics for research purposes,[36] that abortuses have had their chest wall cut to observe the heartbeat,[37] and that scientists have cut off the heads of foetuses and kept blood circulating through them.[38]

In the UK and Australia, foetal experimentation is governed by the medical profession which has formulated advisory group guidelines; in the US, there is governmental regulation in the form of the Department of Health, Education and Welfare (HEW) guidelines.[39] The UK practice means that decision making in this sphere is exclusively in the hands of the medical profession, whereas the US practice brings into the monitoring committees lawyers, the clergy, ethicists and lay people. In matters of ethics, the community will not be as well served as it could be, by leaving decision making entirely in the scientists' hands. The US guidelines prevent experimentation on the pre-natal foetus unless the father and mother are legally competent and give their consent, the father's consent not being required if his identity or whereabouts cannot be ascertained. By contrast, there are no such prerequisites under the UK guidelines. If a foetus is scheduled for abortion, in utero experimentation is not banned outright by the HEW guidelines but is prohibited by the UK guidelines.

Australia leads the world in research on ectogenesis (the development of the embryo outside the uterus), with Monash University as its leading centre. At present, embryos are not kept alive outside the human body for more than about forty-eight hours at the Monash centre, for ethical reasons and because the possibility of defects increases. Longer periods, however, have been reported in the US and in Italy. US researchers are reported to have kept an embryo alive for several days. When the Italian researcher, Dr Daniele Petrucci, reported that, after keeping the embryo alive for several weeks artificially, his experiment had failed and he had 'terminated it', there was an outcry, and the Pope, reinforced by strong public opinion, called for a halt to such experimentation.

The full-term test-tube baby, that is, one grown to full term in the laboratory, is perhaps still many years from us, but in the next few years scientists in different countries will attempt to keep embryos alive in the laboratory. Some will keep them alive longer than is possible at present, and grave issues will then arise, because unsuccessful experiments will need to be terminated. If this occurs on a large scale, with several dozen fertilized embryos being grown simultaneously, the community will need to express its views.

One of the aspects of the Universal Declaration of Human Rights which needs elucidation is the definition of a human being. When it is possible to nurture the foetus in the laboratory entirely, routine 'decantation' rather than the drama of 'birth' will precipitate the baby into the world, and we will have no convenient 'event' to protect us from reaching a decision on its legal status.

A US advocate of liberalized abortion laws, Dr Bernard Nathanson, who performed 60,000 abortions in one of America's biggest abortion clinics, has recently changed his views on the subject and written a book called *Aborting America*, with a view to persuading people to a new view of the intrauterine person. Dr Nathanson believes that in five years there will be foetus farms in which fertilized eggs extracted from the uterus will be cultivated in large quantities.[40] When such a practice becomes more general, the rights of a woman wishing to have an abortion will not necessarily be in conflict with those of the foetus. Both rights could be recognized, and the woman would be able to determine what should be done with her body while at the same time not denying the foetus the right to life. Pregnancies could be detected within nine days of conception, and the extraction of the foetus could be a fairly routine operation.

The problem of nurturing thousands of babies in laboratory conditions raises a host of human rights issues of a different nature, such as the problem of the point in time when the foetus is recognized as a viable human being, the destruction of defective foetuses, and state control.

Conception, hitherto a preserve of nature, is now wide open to human intervention by procedures which have been described as the substitution of the laboratory for the connubial couch. The emotive connotations of such language are strong, but as with so much at the heart of the concept of humanness, the emotional and moral factors blend into each other and collectively exercise a significant impact on the legal issues.

Artificial insemination procedures, first practised on horses and cattle for the purposes of selective breeding, have firmly established themselves in the area of human fertilization.

One estimate, over a decade ago, placed at a million the number of citizens in the US who owed their existence to artificial insemination. In Australia, about 600 couples are treated each year for infertility by artificial insemination, with a success rate of between 50 and 60 per cent, so that there are already several hundreds of people owing their existence to artificial insemination.

As in some other areas, legal problems proliferate. Is the artificial impregnation of a married woman by sperm other than her husband's adulterous? Is the resulting child illegitimate? Is the husband under any duty to support the baby, or must the donor father do so? Should the number of inseminations from a donor's sperm be limited so that his duty to support it is realistic? How is the births' register to record paternity? Must the sanctioning of artificial insemination be by the state and, if so, on what principles? What is the liability of a physician or donor who provides defective sperm and brings into being a child who becomes a liability to the state or an emotional strain on its 'parents'? A child conceived by a married woman through artificial insemination has been held to be illegitimate in Illinois, for example, while the California Supreme Court has castigated as 'patently absurd' the view that artificial insemination and adultery are to be treated analogously.[41] Many years ago, the Ontario Supreme Court spoke of artificial insemination by a donor as a 'monstrous act of adultery', involving as it did the surrender to a person other than the husband of the reproductive faculties of the guilty person. Adultery was in the court's view not confined to the act of sexual intercourse, but its essence lay in introducing into the husband's family a false strain of blood.[42] Legislation has intervened subsequently in California and other US states to give legality to artificial insemination by a donor in the case of consenting married couples and to legitimize the children thus conceived.[43]

This situation shows how old moulds of adultery and family law may need to be broken up, and a new set of basic principles evolved to deal with what is in essence a new set of problems. We have moved far from the extreme view of Pope Pius XII who condemned as sinful artificial insemination by a donor husband.[44]

Children born as a result of artificial insemination by donor of unmarried, widowed, divorced or separated women raise social and psychological issues which have to be clearly thought out. The community needs to resolve whether a person capable of procreating a healthy child should have the right to procreate one, and whether, as far as possible, a child should be born into a traditional family. In other words, the community must give the law a policy decision on whether it has any objection to the deliberate placement of children in fatherless homes. Some case law of the early 1970s foreshadows an answer, where the US courts pronounced the right of the individual *married or single*, to be free from unwarranted government intrusion into matters so fundamentally affecting a person as the decision whether to bear or beget a child,[45] but the law, without contributions from the community, is as yet unprepared to offer affirmative answers to this question. Adoption law prevents an adoptive child being placed in a home of an unmarried, widowed or divorced person of either sex. Should this principle guide the doctor of whom artificial insemination by donor is requested?

The need for the husband's consent, so important to apparent paternity, clashes with the married woman's right to have control over her body. Traditional principles of adultery circumscribed a married woman's rights in this regard, but in many jurisdictions the law has moved away from the analogy of artificial insemination by donor with adultery. At the same time it seems unjust to the husband to presume that children born during his marriage are his.

The physician's role is more complex. If he or she is consulted confidentially by the woman, is he or she in conflict between ethical code and legal duty? Does the uninformed or unwilling husband have a legal action against a physician who administers artificial insemination by donor to his wife?

Centuries of family law have been based on the concept of Christian marriage, and social attitudes have reflected the law's heavy penalization of illegitimate children. Change in community attitudes to illegitimacy is reflected in legislation such as New Zealand's *Status of Children Act* which in 1969 abolished legal discrimination against children born out of wedlock. The United Nations has likewise made a special study of the disabilities of children born out of wedlock, and world opinion is changing. Artificial insemination by donor procedures will force a fresh examination of this issue.

In Vitro Fertilization and Embryo Transfer (IVF and ET)
It is now possible for eggs extracted from a female's ovaries and placed in laboratory receptacles to be fertilized in the laboratory and the embryo to be implanted in the uterus.

The technique, thought to be a remote possibility a decade ago, attracted world headlines when Louise Brown was born in England following in vitro fertilization (IVF) and embryo transfer (ET). Several babies, conceived by IVF and ET followed in Australia and England. By March 1982, there were 1,211 couples on the IVF programme at Monash University's Queen Victoria Medical Centre of whom 300 were currently being treated. Waiting lists in Australia vary from six months to three years. There is such a high demand at present from the Australian community that overseas patients are excluded from the Monash IVF clinic if they have an IVF centre near them and can attend it.

Some important ethical questions are raised by the success of this procedure and the implications it has for the possible control over the creation of life.

Are twelve fertilized human eggs, for example, lying frozen in a solution of liquid nitrogen in a Melbourne hospital 'human life'? The West German Constitutional Court would tend to hold that they are, in view of their ruling that abortion is an act of killing. The US Supreme Court would probably answer that they are not.

The question is not academic. Should surplus fertilized eggs be destroyed? Should they be used for purely experimental purposes? Should they be used as the prototype of a more extensive experiment to produce a thousand eggs? Who determines these matters? Should the eggs be indefinitely stored until they can be used at any time up to even 400 years later, the theoretically possible limit? The Monash team is extremely sensitive to these issues which have been the subject of seminars, discussion groups, dissertations and media programmes, but the ethical issues will not receive such meticulous attention in every centre of research.

Major ethical and theological issues add complexity to the legal problems. Is the reproduction of humans without normal heterosexual intercourse objectionable on religious grounds? Does the effective separation of procreation and love impair the institution of the family? Are people usurping a function of God without the knowledge or wisdom that should accompany that function? Where can we find the answers?

Constitutions? The US Supreme Court's inability to accord human status to the foetus under the constitution has led to attempts to amend the constitution to state that life begins at the moment of fertilization. The amendment is unlikely to succeed. The West German Federal Constitutional Court gives us a supporting view. Most constitutions are silent on the subject.

The churches? The Roman Catholic Church has opposed any form of intervention in the processes of the creation of human life. Relying on the Papal Encyclical, *Humanae Vitae*, the Roman Catholic Archbishop of Melbourne has stated that God has bound the transmission of human life to the conjugal sex act: 'If science helps only to accomplish the marital act or to continue a marital act already initiated, then there is no problem; but if science seeks to exclude or substitute the marital act, the scientific action is not licit.'[46] The Archbishop argued that the embryo must be regarded as a person, never as an object, and questioned the moral right of doctors to embark on a procedure which placed them in the predicament of having to destroy or freeze surplus embryos. Jewish and Islamic theologians seem prepared to declare the practice permissible as long as the husband's sperm is used to fertilize the ovum. Other religious organizations are ranged on both sides of the debate.

Doctors? Doctors supporting such research rely heavily on the medical ethic of the relief of suffering.[47] They argue that the technology arose from requests to treat infertility, and that tubal grafts or transplantation have not yet produced one live healthy baby. IVF is a therapy for resolving personal suffering caused by infertility. Doctors also argue that in discussing the concept of reverence for life, distinctions must be made between the two-cell embryo at the moment of fertilization and the foetus at a later stage of development.

Political parties? The debate waxes hot in the political arena, particularly in New Zealand, where the definition of the beginning of human life was bitterly disputed.[48]

Ethicists? The Australian National Health and Medical Research Council's working party on ethics in medical research submitted its first report in August 1982. It took into account the Helsinki statement on research involving human beings, relevant Australian legislation, and overseas recommendations and guidelines, as well as ethical judgements already made in Australian research institutions. The working party agreed that uninhibited research on gametes (mature sexual cells) and fertilized ova was not acceptable, but agreed that infertile couples had a right to seek and obtain treatment. The doctor's role was to help them, no less than to relieve disease and suffering in people whose health is impaired in other ways. This would apply where the sperm was donated by a marriage partner, but artificial insemination outside the marriage relationship raised major social and legal issues which the committee considered to be beyond its competence. Among its specific recommendations were that embryonic development *in vitro* beyond the stage at which implantation would normally occur is unacceptable, that an embryo should be regarded as belonging to the donors, and that ovum donation to an infertile recipient should, within specified limits, be permissible. The working party found the issue of surrogate motherhood (where the woman did not intend to accept motherhood after birth of the child) difficult to resolve.

In relation to freeze preservation of surplus embryos, the report notes that long-term storage is likely to be distasteful to the community and that it is undesirable for embryos to be stored beyond the time of reproductive need or competence of the female donor. It also suggests that unimplanted embryos should ordinarily be discarded ten years after freezing.

Researchers? Professor Carl Wood, head of Monash University's IVF team, has expressed a fear that the concerted move against IVF by church leaders might cripple the programme. Professor David Scott of the Monash Medical School says that there should be careful thought before the brakes are put on researchers in the biomedical field. The scientists, while conceding the need for a study of the issues involved, seek objective inquiry rather than emotional discussion of the issues.

Patients? Many couples find the long waiting period frustrating and annoying. Fifty-seven of the 1,211 couples who entered the Monash programme have discontinued without giving reasons. On the other hand, the satisfaction of a successful patient appears from the following remarks of Jan Brennan, who gave birth to her baby, Pippin, with the aid of the Monash IVF team. She expressed these sentiments at the Monash Bioethics Centre's Conference on 11 March 1982:

My feelings when I was told over the phone by Sister Jillian Wood that . . . it was almost certain I was pregnant were ones of disbelief, amazement, joy and thousands of other feelings combined . . . Since Pippin's birth she has been an eternal source of happiness and delight . . . How empty our lives would have been without her . . . I still (at seven months) look at her with wonder and awe . . . We will be eternally grateful to the IVF team whose dedicated work made it all possible.

Jan could not have babies naturally because both Fallopian tubes had been removed after a massive infection. She is and has from childhood been a Catholic.

The legal issues involved in such procedures include the privacy of the sperm donor's genetic data, the regulation of sperm banks, the conditions of sperm donation, the prevention of medically unfit donees receiving sperm, the prevention of sperm storage and donation by those with defective genotypes, and the prevention of trafficking in sperm.

If in the past some societies were matriarchal because maternity was a fact but paternity only an opinion, how will society need to reorganize itself when maternity is only an opinion and paternity has ceased to have any force as a principle of social organization? Will we see the state as a true and omnipotent guardian, with doubtful biological parents hovering behind it for the performance of some delegated duties of sustenance and education?

A factor adding to the complexity of the picture is the increasing tendency of the courts to invest the unborn foetus with rights, not merely in the traditional field of criminal law, but also in property and in tort.[49] The rights of the foetus to proper control of the experimental stages preceding its reaching full term will be increasingly recognized, and the future will throw up many new claims: for example, that the choice of parentage was negligent, the choice of genes inappropriate, or the laboratory procedures defective. There will also be claims, already foreshadowed in current litigation relating to 'wrongful life', that the 'creator' had no mandate from the creature to bring him or her into existence and that the former is thus responsible for all the unwanted suffering the latter undergoes during life.

In my view, the conflicts involved in the order of their importance are:

In favour
● IVF and ET are therapy for the relief of suffering caused by infertility.
● The decision is not taken by doctors alone but by a hospital ethics committee including patients and lay people.
● The experiments have been successful so far.

- There is no satisfactory alternative procedure, for example, tube grafts.
- A two-cell fertilized egg is not entitled to the same protection as an embryo.
- Nature is itself wasteful of fertilized eggs, only a fraction of which are implanted in the uterus amd fewer still carried to full term.
- The law draws distinctions between foetuses in different stages of development.
- Excess embryos produced by the procedure can be saved from destruction by freezing.

Against
- Even a genuinely therapeutic procedure is unacceptable if it has adverse social repercussions.
- Laboratory misadventure is possible.
- There is no ascertainable point of time when the embryo changes to human form.
- It is possible that as a result of the procedure human life is wantonly destroyed because there is uncertainty about the human status of the fertilized egg.
- The procedure involves the production of excess embryos which must then be destroyed.
- The ethical issues start at the moment of fertilization.
- The technique may lead to further foetal experimentation using embryonic tissue.
- The foetus is involved in research procedures to which it has never consented.
- Scientists have no right to make judgements about bringing lives into being.
- These procedures substitute artificial means of procreation for the marital act and are not licit.
- People should not interfere with the processes of creation.

Sperm and Ova Banks
Artificial insemination and IVF open up a demand for the ready supply of fresh sperm. Uncertainties about the immediate availability of fresh sperm from suitable donors has led to research on methods of preservation.

The absence on combat duty in Vietnam of large numbers of US servicemen gave impetus to the improvement of techniques for freeze-preservation of sperm. Servicemen likely to be injured in combat could still hope for the impregnation of their wives with their own sperm. The maximum span of 300 days between the death of the father and the birth of his child was now extended without limit, affecting laws on maintenance, legitimacy, inheritance, and paternity.

It can no longer be assumed that only children born before or within nine months of a man's death are his only issue for the purposes of succession. A will leaving property to the children of X may never be able to be fully implemented according to the wishes of the testator, and one may never be able to say with certainty that a particular person died childless.

Sperm banks, storing for many years the sperm of a donor with some unique abilities, may, with the passing of years, add a premium to the cost of such sperm.

A crop of questions will arise for which traditional legal principles will prove inadequate. Will fertilized embryos be bought from a bank with their genetic history provided, as is now possible with seedlings from a nursery? Will orders be placed in advance by prospective foster parents for the creation of a fertilized embryo with predetermined characteristics that are valued by the purchaser? Will commerce and industry equip themselves with stocks of genetic material for the supply of anticipated orders from the wealthy and the powerful? Will Toffler's vision be fulfilled of spouses postponing having children until their careers are completed and then buying embryos to raise in their retirement?[50]

On 2 March 1980, Robert Graham, a businessman in California, held a press conference at his ranch to explain a scheme for providing intelligent women with sperm donated by scientists who had won a Nobel prize.[51] He traced the idea to a concept evolved by a 1946 Nobel prize-winning geneticist, Dr Hermann Muller, who had advocated opening a sperm bank in which donations from brilliant men would be stored until after their deaths and then offered to selected women who wished to increase their chances of producing exceptionally bright children.

The Graham plan immediately ran into criticism that it was capable of abuse in the form of social manipulation, and some critics referred to Hitler's dream of creating a master race. When questioned about the number of Nobel prize-winners who had donated sperm, Graham answered, 'precisely three'. Since then the bank has reportedly been active and its first super babies have been, or are about to be, produced, one of them to a gifted female PhD through the sperm of a brilliant computer scientist.

Although sperm banks are run by private firms in the US, it is unlikely to occur elsewhere, where they will probably continue to be controlled by governments or semi-government authorities. In either case, there seems to be a need for guidelines or regulations on selection, storage, distribution, indexing, and privacy. Value judgments will also be necessary; for example, is particular sperm worthy of storage and is a particular recipient worthy of donation?

In Australia, six sperm banks are in operation. Half of them operate on public funds, and half are private, although not profit making. They are all run professionally, according to the highest ethical standards, controlled as they are by responsible medical personnel.

There is nothing to prevent the commercialization of sperm banks, however, and if a private organization wants to open a sperm bank, there is no legal impediment. Professional guidelines may be insufficient to meet such a situation, and legislation will be called for.

At present, the sperm banks function on the basis of complete privacy for the donor and donee. The donee does not know from whom the sperm has been obtained, although elaborate information about the donor's physical characteristics and medical history would be available to the bank. If the operation of sperm banks fell into private hands, the greatest vigilance and regulation would be necessary to meet the standards that now depend on medical and scientific integrity.

All that has been said in relation to sperm banks will apply to ova banks when the removal and storage of ova become as commonplace as the storage of sperm.

Genetic Engineering

In September 1981, the world heard of the first successful transfer of a gene from one animal species to another: from rabbits to mice. The gene transferred was one directing the manufacture of a part of haemoglobin, the oxygen-carrying component of blood. Dr Thomas Wagner of Ohio University, the biologist who headed the work, was reported to have forecast the use of this method in animal breeding within twenty years 'with major implications for the animal industry'.[52] He saw the medical uses as probably further away as one needed to be sure that the newly induced genes were acting as expected and not causing harm.

This is a timely warning of the dangers of transferring the traits of one creature to another, first in animals and then possibly in humans, because the techniques could be used to transfer genes from different species to make new animals. Indeed, the work done by Dr Wagner for a Denver firm called Genetic Engineering Inc. includes a scheme to produce 'three-parent cattle', which are cattle with added genes from an otherwise unrelated bull or cow to confer some valued quality, such as faster growth or more milk production. The same method could conceivably be applied to humans; for example, to give an insulin producing gene to an infant with a family history of diabetes.

New techniques of this sort raise the question of patent rights. Already patent rights have been recognized in new species of plants and in new microbes produced as a result of recombinant DNA experiments.[53] If the same principle is invoked for new animal creations, rights of proprietorship become attached to living things in hitherto unprecedented ways. Where do you draw the line? The concept of private property clearly needs modification in this area, but the commercial interests which finance such research for private profit are not likely to concede such rights without a contest.

Rights of the Unborn

The rights of the unborn child is an area under rapid legal development. The Victorian case of *Watt* v. *Rama* established new concepts of duties to the unborn child.[54] In that case, the court held that damages could be awarded to a child for brain damage caused through an injury, before its birth, to its pregnant mother in a road accident.

The courts have been leaning increasingly in recent years towards recognizing such rights in the unborn child, which come to maturity when it is born. This is an interesting trend when viewed against the background of an increasing denial of rights to the unborn foetus, in relation to abortion.

In another pioneering Victorian case, in August 1981, it was decided that a baby born eight years after a negligent act was not debarred by lapse of time from suing for damage. In that case, a blood transfusion of an incompatible blood type after a car crash in 1967 had caused a serious blood condition which affected the mother's pregnancy in 1975. Unlike the position in *Watt* v. *Rama*, this case involved injury to the mother long before conception. No Australian or UK case until then had gone so far, and it opened the possibility of a legal duty being recognized towards children of Vietnam veterans with defects caused by chemical sprays to which their fathers had been exposed.

Such developments will be of special significance in the field of genetic engineering in forcing the law into evolving remedies for pre-natal damage caused through biomedical research.

In the US, case law, originally unconnected with genetic experimentation, foreshadowed the concept of 'wrongful life'. In *Zepeda* v. *Zepeda*, an illegitimate child sued his father for fraudulently inducing his mother to have sexual relations with her on promise of marriage.[55] The father was already married, and the child claimed damages for deprivation of an ordinary home life and for the stigma of being born a bastard. While refusing relief in the case before it, the court predicted such later happenings as genetic malformation resulting from radiation, sperm banks, cloning, and chemical interference with foetal formation and suggested that in such instances an action for wrongful life could be brought.

The idea underlying this concept is that people do not choose to be born, but if born have a right to be born without basic defects. If children are born with basic defects which were preventible except for blameworthy conduct on the part of those responsible for their births, they would conceivably have a cause of action for wrongful life. A child born deaf and dumb or deformed owing to rubella, where the mother's rubella was not diagnosed correctly and the child not aborted, is a possible case of 'wrongful life'.

A series of US cases denied wrongful life actions to children. In 1980, however, there was a major breakthrough,[56] when a child born with the hereditary Tay-Sachs disease brought a wrongful life action against medical laboratories through whose negligence the parents were not informed that they were carriers of the disease. The California Court of Appeal reversed the trial court's dismissal of the case.

It is useful, in the context of wrongful life, to consider government obligations towards children born with serious defects. The community has a responsibility for these children, who at present are dependent largely on the good fortune of a concerned parent.

In Canada, Justice Lamont in *Montreal Tramways* v. *Leveille* put the matter clearly when he said:

If a right of action be denied to a child it will be compelled, without any fault on its part, to go through life carrying the seal of another's fault and bearing a very heavy burden of inconvenience without any compensation therefor.[57]

This principle has now been endorsed by legislation in the UK by the *Congenital Disabilities (Civil Liability) Act* of 1976. This act entitles a child born alive with a disability caused by someone's fault to receive compensation.

Although there is as yet no Australian decision on this matter, a recent UK case is likely to be helpful in formulating the Australian law. In that case, an infant who was disabled as a result of an infection of rubella suffered by her mother during pregnancy claimed damages from the health authority and a doctor. She claimed that but for the negligence of the defendants the mother would have had an abortion which would have prevented the child from having suffered a life of debilitation and distress. The lower court held that the child had a reasonable and arguable claim for having been born with deformities, but on appeal it was held that the child's claim was contrary to public policy as being a viol-

ation of the sanctity of human life. The court also found difficulty in evaluating non-existence for the purpose of awarding
damages. Her claim was a claim not to be born at all, a claim
for 'wrongful entry into life' or 'wrongful life'.

If the claim was to succeed, this meant that there was a
duty to take away life. Although the doctor could lawfully
have terminated the life of the foetus, it did not follow that
the foetus had a legal right to die. It would mean regarding the life of a handicapped child as not only less valuable
than the life of a normal child but so much less valuable that
it would not be worth preserving. This would lead to the
proposition that a child had a right to be born perfect or not
at all and would open the courts to claims by children born
handicapped against their mothers for not having had an
abortion.

As opposed to wrongful life actions, wrongful birth
actions are actions brought by parents alleging that the birth
of their child injured them. In a US case, parents sued their
doctors for negligently failing to inform them that the
mother, aged thirty-eight, carried a high risk of bearing children with chromosomal abnormalities.[58] Their child was
born suffering from Down's syndrome. The New Jersey
Supreme Court held that the complaint stated a legally recognizable claim to wrongful birth.

Indeed, there are cases where the courts have even recognized an action for damages where a healthy but unwanted
baby has been born owing to the physician's failure to diag-
nose a pregnancy.[59] The damages claimed were the pain, suffering, and expenses associated with the birth and upbringing
of the child.

Into the Future

We already see glimmerings of pre-ordained sex, baby factor-
ies, reproducing without males, man-animal transplants,
cyborgs (hybrids of man and machine – from cybernetic
organisms), cryonic suspension ('deep freezing' human
beings), arresting death, raising a breed of hyper-intelligent
individuals, and brain-computer links. Biological engineers
have begun the task of human genetic mapping, the iden-

tification and location of each gene along the forty-six human chromosomes. Parthenogenesis, which will produce an individual of the same sex as its parent but not a twin of its parent, and cloning, which will produce an exact copy of the parent, are already the subjects of experimentation with non-human subjects. Fatherless reproduction has already taken place in the world of frogs. New worlds of duplicate maternity and duplicate paternity are just around the corner.

Some of this research will be successful only in the distant future. Much of it will succeed before the century is out. All pose problems which call for consideration now.

The Full-Term Test-Tube Baby

The authentic test-tube baby, nurtured in the laboratory from conception to maturity, has not yet appeared. There is no doubt, however, that researchers in many laboratories are attempting to extend the period of laboratory gestation and that slow advances will be achieved. If we reach the stage of full-term laboratory gestation, all human rights discourse will change dramatically, for as 'decantation' takes the place of birth many basic legal landmarks will disappear.

The process of birth or delivery has from the beginning of the race provided us with a physical event which marks the beginning of life. At what stage 'humanness' attaches to the foetus undergoing laboratory gestation is impossible to answer.

In the process of perfecting the techniques, many experiments will need to be terminated. The community must decide its attitude to thousands of embryos being destroyed at various stages of their development.

Ten years ago this passage appeared in a Hastings Centre report:

The moral issue of embryo manipulation is so great and of such importance to the course of the history of man, that nothing short of a consensus of the scientific communities involved would be needed before proceeding . . . one can only hope that the first baby fertilized *in vitro* would be produced as the endpoint of a collective and public effort of responsible scientists, and not as the premature experiment of a single physician or scientist.[60]

The warning passed unheeded, and the reality came to pass without any of the suggested safeguards. Ten years from now, will writers be pointing out that other warnings about carrying foetuses to full term *in vitro* were similarly disregarded and that the reality is upon us without community consultation?

Selective Breeding

The attempts of the Nazi regime to breed a master race were translated into several programmes. Among these were the compulsory sterilization of epileptics, the feeble minded, victims of hereditary blindness and deafness, manic depressives, and severe alcoholics. Dangerous and habitual criminals were castrated, and marriage was forbidden in cases where one of the parties suffered from a dangerous physical or mental condition. The world greeted information about these Nazi programmes with abhorrence, and any suggestions of using genetic techniques to breed a superior race of people have been strongly opposed.

Some writers have pointed out, however, that with selective breeding it is possible to eliminate or reduce some of the afflictions which have lowered the quality of life for many.

This debate is not likely to occur in the context of breeding a 'master race', but to be viewed rather in terms of progressive steps to be taken to reduce the incidence of inherited disease. It will be argued that those who wish to free their offspring from the possibility of genetic disease should not be denied the right to do so.

It is already possible to increase the possibility of reproducing desired characteristics by resorting to artificial insemination. Sperm banks offer this facility, and a greater range of desired qualities is likely to be offered in the future. Such selective breeding on the part of individuals is likely to grow with the greater realization of the resources and techniques that are available. There is probably little the law can do to arrest such a drift which, even if it grows dramatically, is unlikely to affect more than a small section of the population.

What will be more at issue, however, is not individual breeding or 'gene shopping' programmes but selective breeding. If the incidence of a particular gene-borne disease, such as sickle cell anaemia, reached alarmingly high proportions in a group, it could become a matter of public policy whether compulsory action should be taken to limit the transmission of this defect. As available resources become the subject of increasing competition, the right to procreate of a person transmitting a genetic defect will be determined by public policy. With more effective screening programmes, and improved technology, these people will be readily identifiable, and it will become increasingly difficult to resist the argument that their procreation rights should be curtailed.

Once this stage is reached, there is a danger that the border between preventing the transmission of genetic disease and preventing the transmission of undesired qualities, such as laziness, stupidity, proneness to alcoholism or criminal conduct, will become blurred.

As we approach the stage where genes can be tampered with (happily still remote), the issue will become more momentous, for if genes can be mixed according to a desired prescription, many fundamental assumptions relating to responsibility and humanness will fall away. The danger will be multiplied several-fold when the state enters the field.

When the benefits of selective breeding are already used for various animal species, why should the benefits of selective breeding among humans be withheld?

This is an issue on which it will be necessary for populations to make choices. Concepts of the dignity and integrity of the human personality and religious concepts deeply ingrained in various cultures and traditions will range themselves in opposition to such propositions, but popular sentiment may work against them.

So far, the generation of life outside the body has not been significant enough to require state intervention. Mass cloning once achieved cannot be left in private hands and will demand state control. Indeed, it would be essential that cloning be the subject of international rather than national control.[61]

The greatest danger to be guarded against is that the state will not only be the controller but also the initiator of these processes. Considerations of eugenics will no doubt be advanced as initial justifications, but considerations of power, state organization, and self-perpetuation will then emerge. Dominant groups will have the technology and the legal apparatus to perpetuate themselves and obliterate others. Selected racial or physical types could preponderate.

Once state intervention becomes a reality, it becomes difficult to define and impossible to police which person or what quality is to be reproduced.

The basic legal issues become evident in the light of judicial pronouncements on family life and the importance of preserving a person's right to control his or her marital privacy and the right to procreation. In the language of the US Supreme Court:

The entire fabric of the Constitution and the purposes that clearly underlie its specific guarantees demonstrate that the rights to marital privacy and to marry and raise a family are of similar order and magnitude as the fundamental rights specifically protected.[62]

So also: 'Of this whole "private realm of family life" it is difficult to imagine what is more private or more intimate than a husband and wife's marital relations.' [63]

We have already faced some of these problems with artificial insemination by donors and with techniques of IVF and ET. But what we are about to witness are these problems posed on an infinitely larger scale. In a detailed legal investigation into the implications for individual liberty of state power over human fertility, an eminent researcher observed:

In coming decades the right of the individual to live, love and procreate will be put in issue as never before in human history. The pressure of supposed necessity will create a great temptation to sacrifice the individual and his family and sexual freedoms. As has been shown, the biological revolution will create new powers for man, but these powers may also be used to limit individual freedom. We may some day accept or even demand the use of these powers to control human fertility, but we must give serious consideration to the possibility that freedom may not survive the loss of individual choice over the roots of human existence.[64]

Mind Manipulation

Genetic science is not the only technology that can be used for social moulding. As social unrest escalates in the years ahead, with population explosions and unemployment, the temptation to use mind manipulation technologies will grow. The possibilities are not unreal. There are philosophers and medical staff who believe that such procedures can legitimately be invoked.

Professor B. F. Skinner has argued in *Beyond Freedom and Dignity* that it is our duty to use technology to structure a better human being. Professor Jose Delgado, a pioneer of electrical brain stimulation techniques, has argued in *Physical Control of the Mind: Towards a Psychocivilised Society* that at this critical point in the evolution of man the mind can be used to influence its own structures, functions and purpose, thereby ensuring both the preservation and the advancement of civilization.

A major difficulty with both these contentions, even if they were ethically acceptable, is the impossibility of keeping the technology away from the unscrupulous, and the lack of a means of controlling the controllers. It is true the knowledge is in the hands of a skilled profession, but that profession cannot adequately regulate itself, and its very expertise operates as a screen to protect it from public surveillance. And these sophisticated new technologies may be too alluring for the power hungry politician to resist. More compellingly, when the human mind is the subject of such external interference, the question, whose standards are to be enforced, becomes crucial. The standards of the community, the patient, the physician, and the rulers of the community all tend to vary at any one time and with the passing of time. A patient moulded in a certain cast today, for example, may be unfit for the changed society he or she must live in in fifteen years.

The need for conformity will so narrow the line between violent behaviour and deviant behaviour that one will merge unobtrusively into the other. Homosexuality, drug addiction, alcoholism, feminism, radicalism, and conscientious objection can all be brought within the net. Eventually, whatever conduct the authority of the day deems to be antisocial can be the subject of 'treatment' for change.

There is danger here in some current legal and social attitudes that tend to class criminality or deviant sexual behaviour as 'sickness' or 'mental aberration'. We often speak of those who so behave, as 'patients' needing treatment, in an effort to take them out of the category of offenders requiring punishment. The humanitarian motives are laudable, but it is a dangerous base for authoritarianism, for if such conduct is caused by sickness, that 'sickness' needs to be treated.

More insidious still are the techniques by which the victim will be convinced that he or she is in need of treatment. Techniques for wearing down people's resistance have been worked out to perfection: solitary confinement, daily needling, false information and evidence that former associates are dissociating themselves are some of them.

Graphic portrayals of the manner in which this has been done have appeared recently in the form of memoirs. Solzhenitsyn tells us in *Gulag Archipelago* of methods of interrogation aimed at breaking down resistance. Zhores and Roy Medvedev in *A Question of Madness*[65] have told us of the manner in which a person can be dragged from his home and family and thrown into a mental hospital where a series of examinations are conducted to find evidence of delusion and brain dysfunction. The use of psychiatry in the USSR as a weapon against political dissidents often results in an arrested 'dissident', who is uncooperative under interrogation, being turned over to the Serbsky Institute of Forensic Psychiatry.

Indeed the psychiatric 'trial' can become a feature of political machinery, as Zhores Medvedev illustrates in his chapter entitled 'Medicine Standing on its Head'. He describes how, after his confinement in the Kaluga Psychiatric Hospital, he was brought before a 'commission' for examination and was later brought before another 'commission' attended by a psychiatrist from Moscow. The questioning covered all facets of his activities and his request to record it was refused. Asked why the questioning ranged over these matters, the questioner replied that 'psychiatrists are interested in all aspects of human activity'. Psychiatry in its perverted forms is very clearly a most convenient vehicle for political purposes.

Unfortunately it is not only in totalitarian frameworks that these abuses are perpetrated, and even with the framework of rigid constitutional protections, there is mounting evidence of such practices. In a California prison, an experiment on the use of anectine to condition aggressive impulses was conducted on a sample of sixty-four inmates. A Senate Committee hearing revealed that five prisoners were included in the project against their express will, and eighteen claimed they had consented only under pressure.[66] The experiment involved muscle paralysis with an accompanying frightening feeling of drowning. It was investigated whether admonitions administered when the prisoners were in this state would help to control their behaviour. The experiment in this instance was performed by doctors in a medical faculty acting in good faith. How much greater the danger might be if the medical officers were themselves officials of the confining institution?

Schools are also possible places of mind manipulation. In the US, it was reported in 1970 that amphetamines were being administered to tens of thousands of school children[67] on the basis that their frenetic behaviour supported a diagnosis of mental illness. Whether these children really suffered from organic brain damage or whether they were merely so over-active as to be the repeated cause of disciplinary problems would be a difficult question to determine.

The current armoury of control mechanisms includes such devices as Schwitzgebels and Stimoceivers. Schwitzgebels, already reportedly used in the US for health monitoring purposes, are electronic devices which are strapped to people, capable of tracking their location and transmitting information on their activities and physical conditions.[68] This can become a potent instrument not only for the beneficent curative purposes for which it was intended but also for monitoring conduct and checking deviant behaviour. With a stimoceiver, the implanted electrodes of which are regulated by remote control, the 'patient' can be made to respond automatically to the pattern of conduct programmed for him or her and operated by a computer. The future may well yield more devices of this nature.

Cloning
The word 'clone' (derived from the Greek word, *klon*, meaning a twig or slip) is used to describe the creation of an iden-

tical replica by the process of asexual reproduction. In 1952, frogs were successfully cloned, raising some possibilities for humans.

Very simply stated, cloning involves the removal of the nucleus of a female sex cell and the substitution in its place of the nucleus of an adult body cell of the individual sought to be duplicated. The egg thus enucleated and renucleated will, when it develops, yield an identical copy of the donor of the nucleus. Cell multiplication occurs when the egg thus renucleated starts to develop as though it were stimulated by the natural processes of fertilization. The experiment in which frogs were cloned yielded exact duplicates of the parent frog in about half of the renucleated eggs but also resulted in frog monstrosities.[69]

The technique is capable of being practised on a massive scale, for the donor can yield a practically unlimited number of body cells for renucleation of enucleated eggs. Skin and intestinal cells provide favoured and unlimited sources.

The progression from the frog to the human requires some breakthroughs, none of them thought to be insurmountable,[70] although they will probably take several decades. The mammalian eggs which will need to be enucleated and renucleated for the cloning of humans are considerably smaller and hence more difficult to manipulate and more susceptible to damage than the amphibian eggs of the frog. New methods involving chemical techniques, however, are being developed for this purpose. Moreover, the interests of animal husbandry in breeding prize cattle and racehorses will carry these techniques forward to the point where, some decades hence, they may be sufficiently improved for the next step of experimentation with the human cell.

Well before the turn of the century, we will need to make up our minds whether this new technology is to be given unbridled rein, whether it is to be controlled and directed, or whether it is to be banned until we feel more competent to handle its problems.

The uniqueness of humans, their freedom to develop their own personalities untrammelled by the need or the desire to imitate or differ from a prototype, and the knowledge of the most intimate personal details and propensities which give substance to the concepts of privacy will be under threat by cloning.

Among the issues we will need to resolve are the right to survival of sub-human experimental mishaps, the accountability to society of those desiring to use the new techniques for reproduction, problems of over-specialization, the possible imbalance in the proportions of males to females, an increase in genetic homogeneity, and increasing state controls which may result. If there is genetic material for the cloning of an Einstein or a Beethoven, will a thousand families compete to install exact replicas of the genius within their family? And if public authority decrees that not more than a certain number of identical replicas be produced, will an embryo genius be produced and marketed surreptitiously with false genetic tags?

Given the secrecy with which much scientific research is now conducted, there is every possibility that the technique of cloning, once perfected, can be carried on in secret. Secrecy need only be maintained for nine months before a series of full-term babies are produced. Who then is to decide that they shall not have all the rights of humans, receiving full and equal protection under the law?

The uranium debate in recent years has produced a consensus in many countries that the decision on its use is for the community to make, after informed debate at all levels. The difficulties of communicating scientific information have not stood in the way of such a debate. Likewise, in this field, the decision belongs to the community. In the field of genetic engineering, cloning is one of the aspects that requires most public discussion.

The arguments in favour of cloning are these:
● It will enable infertile individuals or couples to have children.
● It will allow the reproduction of the genetically superior.
● Sex will be able to be predetermined, producing benefits in certain cases by avoiding some sex-linked genetic diseases.
● Eugenic distribution of biotechnical resources without dependence on the lottery of sexual reproduction will be possible.

● Sets of identical humans for the performance of a desired function would be created.

● It will be possible to produce embryonic replicas, to be frozen and put away as sources of organs for members of the identical set. Such organs would not provoke a rejection on the part of the body cells of the recipient.

● It would reduce 'genetic loading', the process by which increasing medical skill assists the weak and defective to survive and propagate themselves and their defects, to the progressive deterioration of the human stock.

● With the growing radiation hazards to our genetic stock, it will help to stow away undisturbed genetic material for development in the future.

● Cell banks could also store for replication certain racial types of endangered humans.[71]

Although some of these advantages are undoubtedly real, some are of only distant value (as with reduction of the genetic load), and some (such as the creation of sets or of spare part banks) are not likely to commend themselves to liberal democrats.

On the other hand, there are many genuine areas of concern:

● Cloning will break down the family concept and established notions of fatherhood, motherhood and parental rights.

● There will inevitably be an increase in state control over matters of reproduction, and the breakdown of the concept of the right to raise a family.

● The new techniques will be used to mass-create selected types for predetermined purposes. In its most extreme form, this will enable a dominant group to perpetuate its dominance and cause all groups in opposition to reduce and disappear.

● It will break down concepts of individuality.

● It will be an invasion of concepts of privacy.

● A blurring of principles of personal responsibility will occur, because the clonant, being made to a pre-set pattern, is in a sense triggered to react in a predetermined way.

● It will be impossible to 'uncreate' the humans created by

such experiments, including the defective and the grossly deformed.

● It will impair religious values and concepts.

Chimeras

On 15 October 1982, the *Age* reported that Dr Patrick Quinn of the Queen Elizabeth Hospital in Adelaide had been using human sperm to fertilize rat ova. The research, conducted at the University of Newcastle, was intended to enable scientists to observe the constituents of human sperm after it had penetrated the ova. Such information, it was said, would make possible the detection of chromosomal abnormalities and the screening of men for suspected infertility. Fears were expressed immediately that human sexuality was denigrated and that scientists might be on the way to creating hybrids. The assurance that there was no possibility for a hybrid to develop because the human and the rat were so different did not stifle the criticism, and the Principal of the Jesuit Theological College in Parkville condemned the research as 'in vitro bestiality'. Scientists might condemn such reactions as over-emotional, while laymen might condemn such experiments as extremely dangerous. More interaction is needed between both groups.

More significant, because closer to possibility and even more disturbing in its implications, was the report in December 1980[72] that Chinese scientists were working on producing a man/animal symbiont by attempting to cross a human being with a chimpanzee. The object of the experiment, reportedly, was to produce a breed of low-IQ, muscular workers, who would be pliant tools in labour-intensive projects.

The scientific world described the suggestion as fanciful, but responsible researchers in the field of IVF have called on governments to legislate against such abuses.[73] IVF, a distant dream only a decade ago, has been achieved. Hybrids of different species have also been produced. We already have announcements of the successful transfer of a gene from rabbits to mice and of the production of 'three parent cattle' through the introduction of added genes. We cannot shut our minds to the possibility of producing chimeras.

Cryonic Suspension

We have seen that the freezing of sperm makes possible the continuance, even for generations, of a person's reproductive abilities.

In the future, the potential of such research will increase with the possible freezing of the human body for reactivation at a future time. This procedure, which is foreshadowed as a means of forestalling death and projecting oneself into a future age, raises legal problems relating to succession and the indefinite perpetuation of ownership. It is in a sense a reproduction of a current person in a future age and to that extent on the periphery of genetic engineering. Just as cryobanks are already in existence for the freezing of human tissue and organs, this new avenue of profit will also be explored for commercial purposes and will need legal regulation.

Neomort Farms

Postponing death raises its share of legal issues, but these are dwarfed by macabre techniques for making medical use of the legally dead. On 13 May 1976, the *Listener* announced a new series of documentaries that would look at important issues with which science was confronting society. An outline of one of the forthcoming features read:

Rows of legally dead neomorts in bioemporia, still warm, breathing and pulsating, could revolutionize medical research. Instead of pulling out the plug, doctors could, with the aid of sophisticated medical equipment, keep a person's body alive, even when he is considered dead. The cadaver, or neomort, would be an ideal test-bed for new drugs, cancer research, tissue culture, and as a natural organ bank for transplant surgery. What are the moral, ethical and legal questions that arise from this potential for recycling human bodies . . . ?

The obvious practical medical value of such farms will be a potent factor in the pressure for their adoption.

The possibilities of such technological erosions are limitless. The human body stands assailed as never before. Will we rise to its defence now, or for ever more be silent?

Chapter 5

Human Society

Francis Bacon's suggestion in the sixteenth century that science would enlarge 'the bounds of human empire to the effecting of all things possible' seemed for centuries to be continually fulfilled. By the popular nineteenth-century utilitarian yardstick of social welfare – the promotion of the greatest happiness of the greatest number – science had eminently qualified as one of society's greatest boons.

It is still true that science and technology, despite some of their drawbacks, are making major contributions to the quality of our lives. Our awareness of this, however, should not encourage us to relax our watchfulness.

The Technology of Decision Making

There is an increasing dependence on the computer to assemble, classify and store information which is too vast to be dealt with efficiently by people. Already computers are used to make decisions in industry and government. Co-ordinating information, for example, they pour out commands which regulate the movements of trains, assembly lines, and aeroplanes. Political, economic, and military decisions, depending on the co-ordination of complex facts, likewise come out of the computer. It was reported that a computer result was the basis on which the US government decided against the use of atomic bombs in the Korean war and thus contributed to General MacArthur's decision to retire.[1]

Clearly, computers will turn out results which are slanted in favour of those who control them. Not without reason did Norbert Wiener, who was a pioneer in studying the capacity of computers to emulate the human mind, warn that the machine would give new and potentially dangerous powers to powerful people.[2]

Despite the advances in electronics, however, the electronic brain may never entirely replace humans. Its limitations are too numerous to make this possibility anything but fanciful at the moment, although an entirely new computer, built as an analogue to the human nervous system, may soon bring us close to this.[3] Nevertheless, the simulation of human thinking, with the help of computer programs, is being developed. The essential components of the thought process are not words or images but a properly ordered succession of the 'legitimate steps' which are capable of being simulated by computers. The emotional components are not. The computer functioning judicially, for example, may never fully comprehend the human sentiment of love, in a matrimonial dispute; or when functioning executively may not feel the sympathy (or the selfishness or ambition) of a human. The computer's decision will be most impersonal but, without doubt, it will guide, in increasing measure, the human decision-maker's judgment.

The Machine as Social Planner
The ability of the computer to handle simultaneously a large number of variable factors means that the scope of planning is vastly increased both in size and in detail.

Planners are no longer content to plan within an environment. With the help of computer technology, they plan the environment, for example, by designing entire urban areas and developing master plans of traffic control and massive irrigation schemes. The environment can be altered to suit the design where formerly the design had to fit the environment.

There is in this a twin danger. The first is a near total dependence on computer technology. The second is that once such a plan is implemented, the scope for the individual is limited. Such overall schemes call for rigorous conformities; the master plan is dictatorial and expensive.

As technology progresses, the number and the scope of systems thus planned will increase, and the area of operation for the individual will correspondingly decline.

Information Storage

Computers not only make decisions and formulate plans, but also store data on individuals. Many people pass on personal data to government and public instrumentalities such as local government, insurance companies, social welfare organizations, land registration boards, and census, income tax, and education offices. Put together, that information is a complete dossier on each individual. The ability of governments to compile such dossiers puts in jeopardy our rights to independence and autonomy.

In a nationwide radio broadcast in 1972, President Nixon drew attention to the awesome potential of the computer for harm as well as good. In many cases, he said, people were not aware what information was held on record and did not know how to find out; computer banks held information on 150 million US citizens. President Nixon launched an inquiry into the way in which the federal government collected information on people and how that information was protected. 'Adequate safeguards must always stand watch' he said, 'so that man remains the master and never becomes the victim of the computer.' In the years that have passed since this warning, computer power has grown more dramatically than the president foresaw, and the means for controlling it have become progressively more inadequate.

The trend towards centralization means that the merging of these data banks in different government and commercial departments is inexorable. Nothing short of legislation will halt it. If knowledge is power, the tools for marshalling it increase that power enormously.

In the UK and Australia, there is already a nexus between data banks maintained by customs offices, motor registration branches, income tax boards, and the police. In the private sector, data on people collected by credit agencies, insurance corporations and employers can also be collected in a central repository. People's credit ratings are established from just such centralized information.

The sensitive field of medical records is an illustration of the dangers of data banks. Many people undergo comprehensive medical checks from time to time, in which they give medical staff an enormous amount of highly confidential information. There are no adequate guarantees that the information recorded may not be given, for example, to the police. In May 1981, Mr Justice Kirby highlighted this danger in two speeches delivered to the Queensland Medico-Legal Society and the ANZAAS Congress. He drew an analogy with telephone tapping, which was used in Australia for national security but had been extended for use in narcotics surveillance and was now also being requested for police surveillance. The law has so far been ineffective in preventing misuse. Sweden, ahead of the world in this regard, was the first country to require multi-national corporations to apply for permission to store personal data on their employees in other countries. The information, routinely stored by an employer for administration and promotion purposes, would include information on age, marital status, spouse, children, nationality, income, education and areas considered to be sensitive and private, such as health, criminal records, and political sympathies.

This field affects not only people's integrity but also the concept of sovereignty, because there is as yet no effective international embargo on the export of data. Short of international agreement and an international data act, there will be intrusions on privacy, freedom, and individuality. We must legislate to protect the rights of people to data protection.

Combating the Information Tyranny

Fortunately for human freedom, steps have been taken towards data protection by some countries. The Council of Europe finalized a draft convention on data protection on 27 June 1980, bringing to fruition work which began in 1976. The convention reinforces and supplements national data protection legislation which several of its member states had introduced since 1973. An international convention had become necessary to ensure that people in different countries would be offered equal standards of protection and to lay down standards in relation to the escape of data across national frontiers.

The principles guaranteed by the convention cover not

only the quality of the information processed and the proper use of that informaton, but also the physical protection of that data. Data subjects are given the right to know the information stored about them and to demand rectification where necessary. Sensitive data relating to racial origins, political influence, religious or other beliefs, health, sexual life and criminal convictions are not allowed to be the subject of automatic processing unless domestic law provides appropriate safeguards. Derogation from the basic standards is permissible only for major reasons of state interest, such as national security and suppression of criminal offences or for the protection of the rights and freedoms of others, for example, in the interests of freedom of the press.

The convention sets out procedures for mutual assistance between the data protection authorities of different countries and for helping a person in one country to obtain protection from data files held in another.

The convention is a significant first step, but its limited applicability and the lack of universal rules which bind the international community leave most people exposed to an information tyranny which debases their human rights.

It is possible now, and by no means particularly expensive, to collect data in one country, store it in a second, process it in a third and print or display it in a fourth. Keypunching of some Canadian social security data, for example, is done in Taiwan. Large volumes of Australian credit data are stored in computers in Singapore. The fire hazards in every house in many Swedish towns can be flashed in an emergency on a screen on a computer in Cleveland, Ohio.[4] People must be protected from having their credit ratings or medical records called up on a screen in, say, Singapore, Tokyo, or New York. The countries of the Third World are intensely concerned that their vital data, which are stored in affluent countries largely through the activities of the transnational corporations, will be displayed on terminal screens in the major capitals of developed countries.

Australians may have personal data processed in Singapore and not be aware that Australian law has no protection against the information being bought by a person in Singapore. Indeed, as some countries sought to set themselves up in the past as tax havens, there is now a rush to become data havens.[5]

Laws are already overdue in most countries on the lines of the *Swedish Data Act* of 1973 which provides that items will be released for data processing abroad only after special permission has been granted by the data inspectorate. Some years ago the inspectorate stopped data being sent to the UK because its privacy laws were considered to be too weak.

The Council of the OECD has adopted certain guidelines which represent a consensus of basic principles which national legislatures will be able to imitate or adopt. One of their main objectives is to uphold human rights in the sphere of privacy.

The OECD guidelines adopt eight basic principles which recognize that the collection of personal data should be by lawful and fair means and, where appropriate, with the knowledge and consent of the person involved. The personal data should be relevant to the purposes for which they are to be used and should be accurate, complete, and kept up to date. The purpose for which the data are collected should be specified at least by the time of collection, and they should not be used or made available except with the consent of the subject and by authority of law. The data should be protected by reasonable security safeguards. A general policy of openness is recommended on the existence and nature of the data and the identity of the controller. People should have the right to obtain information recorded about them within a reasonable time. They should also have the right to challenge the data recorded and to have incorrect data corrected. The data controller should be accountable for complying with the principles laid down.

One of the more important facets of transborder data flow concerns the exchange of criminal data. Although there is room for the argument that international police co-operation is essential for the suppression of crime and terrorism, there can still be differences between countries on the 'information' which can be passed across national borders. Some of it could be described as essential 'command and control' data, such as the availability of police personnel, and the incidence of crime, but there is a danger that information on criminal records, finger-prints, 'wanted persons' and criminal intelligence (including information held in police data banks) will also be passed on.

Data storage breeds other dangers, for the information stored is so valuable that it becomes a tempting object of theft. Computer crime, a by-product of the computer revolution, has the double attraction of being lucrative and difficult to detect. Its potential for social damage is immense. Ransoms are now being demanded for hijacked computers. As early as 1970, rioting students at New York University took over three halls of a $3.5 million computer installation belonging to the Atomic Energy Commission. Plans for the hijacking had been carefully worked out. When President Nixon announced that the US would move into Cambodia, student protests on university campuses erupted all over the country. After four students at Kent State University were killed by security forces, about a hundred students surged into the hall where the computer was housed. The chairman of the Department of Computer Science was ordered to shut down the machine. Students broke through the locked doors and gained entry to the room containing the key punch machines. A ransom was demanded for the release of the computer, and pledges of up to $15,000 were made. The incident was defused by law enforcement officials who broke into the building.[6]

Security around computer installations will need to be doubled, particularly where the computer houses sensitive information on which national security may depend, and people working in and around a computer will need to be screened with the strictness formerly appropriate only to the safety of a prince or a president.

The larceny of computer information is a crime of increasing frequency. When classified information is stolen, people's private integrity and the public's security is threatened. Such purloining of information, already a common phenomenon in the commercial world, will not be confined to commercial secrets. Official secrets and security information will be among some obvious targets.

There are security devices which make it possible to put certain information beyond the reach of unauthorized people. The computers of stockbrokers connected to the data bank of the stock exchange, for example, can each be fitted with restrictive devices which prevent information of a classified nature from being accessible to such computer users. It is not impossible, with the co-operation of a worker within the data bank, however, to place a 'patch' on the user's connection with the data bank, so that the barrier to certain prohibited classes of information is lifted. This is difficult to detect.

It is said in answer that the code of conduct of computer programmers has been carefully worked out with a deep sense of responsibility on the part of the computer profession. Although the computer profession is to be commended for its outstanding concern for its ethical duties – a concern exceeding that of most other groups of technologists – many computer workers are not members of the governing professional bodies. Australia, for example, has thousands of computer operators and programmers, and in the US those with access to computers and computer technology number over half a million. In such a vast group, the preservation and enforcement of high ethical standards is a near impossibility, despite the dedication of the professional bodies.

It is not difficult to conceive of governments or high officials using their power or influence to extract information of a classified and personal nature, which they consider valuable for their purposes. High government officials, as proved by the Watergate episode, are not above resorting to criminal means for collecting information. Organizations such as the CIA have surveillance tabs on several million US citizens.

Computer crime in organizations is often hidden for fear of damaging the corporate image and hence debasing the value of shares if this were known. Additionally, criminal law and the laws of evidence are inadequate to deal with computer crime. In June 1981, the president of the Victorian Society for Computers and the Law and the head of the Fraud Squad of the Victoria Police drew attention to legal inadequacies in handling computer crime.[7] Among the areas pinpointed were the inadequate definitions of theft by deception, for example, where a credit card is fraudulently used to deceive an automatic telling machine, and there is doubt whether a machine can be deceived; obtaining financial advantage by fraud, for example, where lines are tapped and information fed into another terminal; and causing damage to magnetic disks holding computer records, for example, where an operator wipes out information on a computer memory.

In all these cases the law is unclear and needs amendments to make prosecution and conviction more certain. Where computer abuse straddles national boundaries, with differing data protection laws and penal provisions, prosecution is more difficult.

Information Gathering

The most sophisticated technology for invading privacy is freely on sale. Glossy commercial catalogues advertise a number of interesting devices designed specifically for unobtrusive surveillance. Although the sale of such devices may be illegal in the country of their origin, there is nothing to prevent their international distribution. Among the devices in such catalogues are a standard felt pen which houses a transmitting unit, an ashtray with a microphone that will receive and transmit the faintest words, and a cigarette lighter which transmits conversations a distance of 250 metres. Many electronics firms offer similar facilities undeterred because they are uncontrolled by international law.

In the context of the office, the ordinary electric light bulb is capable of containing a transmitter as is a transmission cord for a power plug. Cocktail olives, matches, wrist watches – even dental fillings – can be implanted with miniaturized devices. More sophisticated devices are available to relay conversations. A light beam bounced off a window pane can be used to reconstruct conversation within it. A laser beam reflected off any object in the room, such as a calendar, which is set in vibration by conversation, can do likewise.[8] A picture or tapestry or wallpaper can be installed with a secret transmitting device pasted into the paper at the back.

In the hands of governments and corporations, these surveillance devices are sinister weapons. Many government and corporation employees live in government- or corporation-owned premises. It poses no problems to employers to install surveillance devices in rooms of apartments to be rented to employees. The extent to which these devices impair privacy has been the subject of United Nations studies and of concern wherever the law of privacy is under review.[9]

Through devising means of scanning customers in department stores, the installation of concealed scanning devices has become an art which defies detection. Concealed cameras can take movies or stills and can adjust themselves to take close-ups of a person in any position in the room. Devices of this nature are commercially obtainable at very moderate prices.

Terrorism has given governments compelling reasons for installing on roof tops or at street junctions an array of surveillance devices which scan and film the junction continuously. These devices, installed initially for important occasions, such as a heads of state conference, are not necessarily dismantled when the purposes for which they were erected end, and their retention is justified on the grounds of crowd control. In Melbourne, for example, surveillance devices installed for the Commonwealth Heads of Government Meeting continue to be used at important junctions long after the conference came to an end.

Tracking techniques perfected during the Vietnam war are being used in peacetime. Thermal detectors, sensitive to variations of temperature as slight as 0.001 degrees Celsius can detect where a person has been. Seismographic warning devices can detect a person's movements on the top storey of a building by the very slight tilt in the building caused by the person's shift of weight.[10] Thermal tracking procedures, devised for guiding missiles, can detect from a distance the extra heat a vehicle generates, and these techniques have been perfected for keeping track of human beings.

With the increased use of magnetized identity cards and the decreasing cost of computerization, it will soon be possible to computerize all public transport. Identity cards may be issued to travellers who will be billed at the end of each month. The computerized storage of this information will make available for instant retrieval all the journeys a person makes by public transport. Entry to buildings can likewise be computerized and recorded, as can the passage over key points such as a bridge or toll gate.

'Bumper beepers' can be used to track motor cars, bicycles or other vehicles by being attached inside the bumper bar of a car or some other concealed part. Miniature transmitters can be sewn into clothing, and radioactive pills or radioactive tracers included in a person's diet.

Computerized facilities for storing and analysing information or people, when added to the scanning devices available, make technological intrusions on privacy nearly complete.

The new technologies of information gathering have bred a psychology of their own. A former president of the Massachusetts Institute of Technology who was also science adviser to President Kennedy[11] marched in anti-Vietnam war demonstrations and wondered afterwards whether he was being watched as a threat or as a dangerous enemy of the state, under continuous surveillance.

Many people operate on the assumption that they are under surveillance. The scientist in question did not allow the possibility of surveillance to inhibit his movements, as he had confidence in the safeguards built into the US judicial system. The average citizen, however, not steeled by such confidence, may suffer much unease at the prospect of being watched. Students, in particular, could feel inhibited from participating in political activities for fear that it might possibly make later job clearance difficult to obtain.

The computer opens up another field of scrutiny unavailable before. Through computer scanning of widely scattered data, it is possible for a computer to detect associations between people and other people or organizations which it might otherwise have been impossible to notice, for example, by scanning bank accounts or mail, or computerized registers of telephone calls.

In a well-known New Jersey case,[12] the state attorney-general sent a memorandum to local officials on civil disorders, calling for the creation of a police intelligence system that would enable law enforcement authorities to keep a tab on individuals and organizations considered potential trouble-makers. The information to be recorded was to cover not only details such as physical description and credit background, but also 'membership, affiliation and/or status with organizations and groups'.

The New Jersey branch of a national civil rights organization tried to have this intelligence system declared unconstitutional, and the trial court viewed such a centralized information system as having a 'chilling effect' on the free expression of political views and on freedom of association. The trial court prohibited the state from compiling this information, a view which was reversed by the New Jersey Supreme Court on the grounds that it would be foolish to deprive the government of its power to deal with the tyranny of lawlessness.

Cable television is another potential source of danger, because along with the cable which enters each home there can be a thin unobservable wire that will transmit information on the programmes being watched in that home. A concealed technological McCarthyism can thus descend upon society unawares.

A new telephone system with Orwellian overtones is TIMS (The Telephone Information Amendment Systems) for which Telecom Australia has given its approval. This new device gives business a long overdue method of traffic analysis which could show the need for more or fewer lines. The system is already in use by some employers. The system at the same time gives employers the capacity to increase their surveillance over their employees, and for this reason attracted the attention of the New South Wales Privacy Committee in 1980. The committee, while recognizing the employer's prerogative to ensure that employees are spending their time on work-related activity, recommended that staff should be fully consulted before any decision was made to install the system, and that every telephone connected to TIMS should carry a notice informing the user that the numbers dialled and the time and cost of the calls would be recorded for management purposes. The system was already in use in 1981 at a leading Sydney hotel.[13]

Technological surveillance is not restricted to the computer. It also extends to intrusions into the human mind and personality. Personality tests were developed to protect nuclear and military establishments.

Frequently, people wanting jobs in the commercial or legal world are required to take personality tests as a condition of employment. Personality tests have spread from the public to the private sector because many organizations, not part of the military establishment, have become dependent on it for funds. These organizations – including some universities – are then forced to screen their prospective employees.

Personality tests are a highly commercialized industry. All manner of tests have been fabricated for all manner of purposes, and experts advise potential customers which test will suit them, or undertake to produce a test which is tailored for them. Mass-produced tests which screen applicants for a variety of jobs are often administered without professional assistance or evaluation, with the result that many tests fail to achieve their objectives. The tests cover aptitude, intelligence, family background, predispositions, achievement, responses to situations, instinctive reactions, sex life, and religious belief.

Much of this information finds its way into records and dossiers which are at the disposal of the employer. The threat of misuse is greater than the threat of leakage, because the data can be misinterpreted by a non-expert and the wrong conclusions kept on record.

When the lives of people and their fortunes depend on the storage of such data, much of which is pseudo-scientific, individual freedom is surrendered at least in part. To have to subject oneself to probing, measuring, and analysis in relation to one's personal attitudes and reactions is a powerful negation of human rights. This is not to say that some measure of psychological testing should not be used for certain types of jobs. Those who activate military weapons or those who, like airline pilots, carry people's lives in their hands, must have some kind of psychological evaluation. But such obvious applications are few. The increasing sophistication of these tests will mean that more areas of privacy will be probed.

Among possible safeguards are requirements that personality tests should be administered only where essential, that their evaluation should be in the hands of adequately quali-fied people, and that the questions asked should not probe any deeper than is essential. Additionally, the questionnaire should have the approval of an authority specially charged with the responsibility of ensuring that these procedures are not misused, and the information should not go on perma-nent record but be destroyed after its immediate use. Com-puter evaluation of data should always be subject to scrutiny in relation to its methodology and a periodical reappraisal guaranteed for the correction of errors.

Stored data should be safeguarded by special security devices and should on no account be released outside the organization, except with the permission of the subject. Every organization using personality tests should be required to report its use of them and obtain a clearance of the test from an appropriate authority. Guidelines should specify sensitive areas such as religious practices, sexual attitudes, and information on one's parents, which should not be per-mitted in tests of any description except where proved to be specifically essential.

Torture is another form of information-gathering. By becoming a normal instrument of government in dozens of countries, torture has become common. Tortures to which prisoners are subjected have been refined by science. Drugs which induce horror, psychological techniques which shatter a prisoner's perceptions of situations and events, and finely graded electrical shocks calculated to cause the most excru-ciating pain have all been supplied to the torturer by science. In the words of Amnesty International's president, an epi-demic of torture is sweeping through the world.

It is known that a variety of drugs used in psychiatric treat-ment can be used for non-therapeutic purposes. Pharmaco-logical torture by which a prisoner is threatened with the use of pharmacological agents is another technique. Short-acting anaesthetic agents, such as thiopentone, are used, as are hallucinogenic drugs, such as LSD, which cause disruption of normal perceptions. The victim does not know which drugs will be given and that some of them may be perfectly harmless. Some drugs used, such as suxamethonium, cause temporary paralysis, and others cause unpleasant symptoms, such as vomiting, as with apomorphine.

A vast amount of scientific research into sensory deprivation techniques carried out during the 1950s has enabled interrogation procedures which in the 1930s took a minimum of six weeks to be reduced to six days.[14]

Traditional KGB methods consisted of surprise night-time arrest, solitary confinement, regimented eating, sleeping and lighting, enforced idleness, and extremes of temperature. These methods led to personal breakdown, and from that point on the extraction of confessions was easy.

The methods used in Northern Ireland in 1971, however, consisted of 'depth interrogation' by the hooding technique in which victims were covered with black hoods like pillow cases, forced to stand against a wall in a search position, supported only on their fingertips and wearing loose-fitting boiler suits, for periods of up to sixteen hours continuously, and returned to this position forcibly when they fell. They were subjected to a continuous, loud, 'white' noise of 85-87 decibels; they were deprived of sleep during at least the first few days of about a week of interrogation; and they were deprived of food except for bread and water at six-hourly intervals. Nearly all those who have been through hooding suffer serious after-effects.[15] Almost all suffer from visual and auditory hallucinations and paranoid delusions, and hardly any of the hooded men appear to have recovered.

Methods of physical torture have likewise been refined so as to induce the greatest physical pain while at the same time leaving few physical scars. Most research, however, centres on mental tortures.

The medical profession has a responsibility in this area. Conflicts of conscience could occur for doctors working in prisons, camps, the armed forces, and the police force. Doctors working in prisons and camps should not be employed by or be primarily responsible to the prison authorities; and medical staff working in the armed forces, the police force or in prisons should be aware of the international conventions on the treatment of prisoners.

Panels of medical experts could be set up to investigate allegations of torture, and international examination centres could be set up to assess the treatment of torture victims.

Stamping out Diversity

Modern technology has played a part in eliminating the diversity which so enriches society. The railway and the telegraph bound together vast territories under a central administration. Broadcasting made the bonding more effective, and satellite transmissions extended uniformity by perpetuating the dominance of certain cultures, especially the American, in programmes beamed to a worldwide audience. International agreements are being reached which aim to prevent subtle cultural infiltration from satellite transmission. Intrusions into people's lives take place through the electronic media in quite subtle and subconscious ways. In many countries, indoctrination in political views is openly carried on through the electronic media.

Such indoctrination takes place not only by governments but also by privately owned media. People with sufficient capital to own the large media organizations naturally have an interest in maintaining the *status quo*, and they will not permit the industry they own to undermine the system which gives them their power. The sophisticated electronic and print technology necessary for survival in the media industry can only be bought by a select few, and the smaller operator, who is more prepared to voice a dissentient view, is driven to the wall. These select few exercise enormous power going far beyond the traditional scope of free speech, a free press, and free opinion.[16]

Competition with the large groups, with all their resources of capital, has become so difficult that in Australia, for example, the numerous fiercely independent regional dailies of the pre-Menzies era have given up the struggle and allowed themselves to be swallowed by the giant groups. Where in 1930 seventeen proprietors published twenty-one capital city daily newspapers, by 1976, three companies – The Herald and Weekly Times Ltd, News Limited, and John Fairfax Ltd – owned or controlled the seventeen capital city dailies which were left. Indeed, Australia is one of the countries most affected by the new technologies in this area, because the concentrations of media power in Australia are, proportionately to population, probably greater than in any industrialized country.

These great media organizations are also linked to major global newsagencies. By satellite transmissions, newsagencies, such as Visnews in London, supply world news film to nearly 200 television organizations in over a hundred countries. Such an agency may thus supply over a thousand million people across the world with the information on which they form their judgments on world affairs. Such news must necessarily be highly selective.

In politics, advertising agencies, relying on their psychological advisers, play a significant role in moulding the television profiles of candidates,[17] a matter of which Australian audiences have become painfully aware through the television build-up of the personalities of Mr Fraser and Mr Hawke no sooner the general election of 1983 was announced. In planning US presidential campaigns, fresh techniques learnt from the manipulation of the US mass consumer market are constantly applied.

The higher the social status of a group, the greater its social and economic powers, and consequently the greater its access to and control over the processes of communication. Modern technology in the communication media thus tends to preserve the *status quo*, and, in this way, it has enabled the media to take the place of church and state in moulding people's opinions and beliefs. Indeed, it places the media in a better position for this purpose than was ever possible by the state or church.

Technology used in this way forces us to re-examine freedom of expression and freedom of the press. The technology available to those who control the media is not directed only against free thought and opinion. It also attacks freedom of trade. Competitive advertising curtails freedom of trading by imposing a heavy entrance fee. When the British soup market was shared by Heinz, Crosse & Blackwell and Batchelor, for example, it was difficult for any other competitor without financial resources for television advertising to break in. When Knorr-Swiss and Campbell Soups entered the race, they were able to pay the fee required, and this triggered off an advertising race which shot annual advertising expenditure to over £2 million.[18] This is small change compared to the advertising budgets of the larger cereal manufacturers, which exceed $100 million each year. In this competition, the small entrepreneur has no chance.

Modern psychology brings new weapons to the aid of this attack on free trade. The media have at their disposal expensively evolved analyses of the hidden factors which help or retard the process of persuasion. 'Warm' colours (for example, red, orange, yellow) are known to make packages seem larger, and 'cool' colours (for example, green, blue, violet) suggest tranquillity and smallness.[19] Bright, intense colours suggest masculinity and hardness, and soft pastel shades suggest femininity. Appeals to sexuality, pride, class consciousness, race and success are built into many advertisements, sometimes quite immorally, of which perhaps the best example is the skill of the tobacco trade in associating their products with health, opulence, and success. These techniques are not limited to commercial advertising. Political promoters and advertisers frequently use them.

Subliminal perception is another weapon of psychology. A fleeting message displayed for so short a period that it is not consciously noted has, through repetition, a strong influence. Internationally, there have been protests against the possibility of satellites being used to beam subliminal messages to unsuspecting people.

Sources of Inequality

The elimination of diversity may at first sight appear to be a technological contribution to social stability. In fact it creates a series of new inequalities. The extraordinary power the machine gives to those who work it is one of these. Their power is unprecedented, neither dependent on force, nor so apparent as to be challenged.

The secretary-general of the United Nations, in his report to the Commission on Human Rights of 9 January 1974, referred to the need to give people an understanding of computer methods or at least the elements of information about programming, so that they would not be at the mercy of experts.

The extent of society's dependence on the technologist was forcefully brought home by the great north-east blackout of 1965 in the US and, more recently, the New York blackout in July 1977, which showed how a comparatively trivial malfunctioning of technology could cripple an entire nation. If that malfunctioning were engineered by a small technological group, it could produce similar results.

In 1976, news reports carried details of a plan by the army to simulate a germ attack on the president and the entire US Congress.[20] These reports claimed that, according to a former Pentagon researcher, army germ warfare experts carried out a simulated assassination of President Nixon and of Congress in 1969, which the secret service, the FBI, and Capitol Hill police did not know was taking place. If there had been a dissident group of technologists within the army who were planning such a move, neither the president nor Congress could have survived.

All societies, capitalist and communist, developed and underdeveloped, accord their skilled technologists a level of reward and recognition which place them in a class apart. Privilege and prestige, thus added to power, complete the new élitism.

The way in which powerful interlocking interests of officials and industrialists protect themselves in Australia can be well illustrated in the area of forestry, where multi-million dollar timber, pulp and woodchip industries have strong links with government forestry services and university forestry departments. An Australian National University researcher has found that these links include informal networks of communication, professional and commercial organizations, clubs, joint conferences, and consultations about appointments.[21] The movement of key people between posts in forest industries and government forest services strengthens the links, and several leading figures in the government forest services (including commissioners of the Forests Commission of Victoria) have taken positions with forest industries on retirement.

The Australian administrative system, by which state cabinets appoint senior officials, including the departmental head responsible for the industry (unlike the UK system, where such appointments are made by an independent Public Services Commission), helps this connection. Where the industry has considerable political and lobbying power, these key appointments can be made in a manner which is acceptable to the industry. The industry's interests then tend to be protected down the line, with powers vested in the politically appointed departmental heads. Regulations such as those of the Victorian Public Service introduced in 1974 make it punishable with dismissal for a state government scientist to criticize departmental policies. Put bluntly, the Victorian administrative system ensures that forests exist primarily for the forest industries.

The researcher has listed a number of instances of suppression of the results of research which did not conform to the needs of bodies with vested interests. These publicized cases, only a small fraction of the total, include such instances as that of a scientist at La Trobe University who spoke out on the question of the spread of cinnamon fungus. The Forest Commissioner of Victoria protested to the university and was informed that university statutes in Australia are framed to allow staff to speak publicly on controversial issues, thereby preserving academic freedom. The stifling of inconvenient scientific opinion is also documented in other areas, such as the chemical and nuclear industries. Together they add up to a pattern of a powerful alliance between technology, industry and the bureaucracy.

The multi-nationals and the military are in command of a considerable proportion of the world's advanced technology. Consequently, technological decisions are dominated by considerations beyond the competence of most voters, and even if they were able to assess such issues, the power structure would operate to keep decision making out of their hands. The incomprehensibility of technology thus offers a smoke-screen, blurring the vision of voter and legislator, and allowing powerful technologists in large industrial and military corporations to make decisions free of controls.

The space programme and the Inter-Continental Ballistic

Missile programme are two examples in the US. Speaking of the Anti-Ballistic-Missile System, Professor Hans J. Morgenthau of the University of Chicago, observed:

The great issues of nuclear strategy, for instance, cannot even be the object of meaningful debate, whether in Congress or among the people at large, because there can be no competent judgment without meaningful knowledge. Thus the great national decisions of life and death are rendered by technological élites, and both the Congress and the people at large retain little more than the illusion of making the decisions which the theory of democracy supposes them to make.[22]

It is not, however, only through their links with the military or the bureaucracy that large corporations achieve a position of authority in a country.

The giant corporations have become world powers in their own right. With revenues far exceeding those of over a hundred members of the United Nations, and with a monopoly of the sophisticated technologies they command, they do business with states too poor to deal with them on equal terms, and wield the threat of withdrawing the technology which those states desperately need.[23]

The inequalities resulting from such financial power are compounded by the veils of multiple corporate registration. Many multi-national corporations function in several countries under several hundreds of separate but interlocking registrations. They market their technology in dozens of legal jurisdictions under a variety of names, making it impossible for a citizen or his or her lawyers to track down those responsible for unleashing some dangerous technology.

Current legal arrangements, then, protect the corporations rather than the citizen and, in legal matters involving a complex of corporate, military and bureaucratic might, it is often academic to talk of the citizen having a right to assert a claim against one of them.

Unemployment

Technology introduces its own sources of instability. On average, a clerk works eight hours a day for 250 days of the year, which is 2,000 hours each year. Through a working life of forty years, he or she accumulates 80,000 hours. The clerical contribution of such a person throughout his or her life can be matched by a computer in four minutes. This means that increasing numbers of people, especially in the developed countries, will find themselves out of work in the twenty-first century. This means that millions of schoolboys and schoolgirls will never have jobs. In the alarming escalation of Australia's unemployment figures, which rose from 370,400 in 1981 to 536,800 in 1982 and are expected to reach 800,000 in 1983, computerization and automation are playing a significant part. As jobs are lost at the estimated rate of one every minute, one hears reports from various industries of a computer or robot displacing anything up to a dozen workers. As the big manufacturing companies struggle to cut production costs, they introduce labor-shedding machinery. During the past two years, Email, for example, cut manual handling and pre-production work on the assembly line by investing in machines. Its workforce has reduced in two years from 8,627 to 7,405, and its general manager has said that 240 jobs in the company have gone as a result of mechanization.[24] Nissan (Australia) has introduced robots to handle operations on its production line, each robot doing the work of several workers. When Australian Paper Mills put in a new paper-making machine at their plant in Marysville, 200 employees were reduced to sixteen.

Work is needed not only as a human right but also, in the view of many, to hold society together. If work is not available to vast numbers of people through no fault of their own, it breeds instability.

Boredom and insecurity are two classic triggers of social unrest. The United Nations foreshadowed this problem many years ago and inaugurated various studies on teaching the use of leisure on a massive scale to people who, by the early years of the next century, will suddenly find themselves with enormous amounts of spare time.

Process workers, long justifying their retention in the workforce because they were cheaper to employ than machines, will find themselves eased out of their jobs by automation and the microchip. The robot, claiming no holidays, worker's compensation or superannuation, will take over from the human worker more and more, working with a steadiness and precision that the human cannot match.

Although it is hoped that some new technologies will stimulate a range of new jobs, this is an optimistic view not widely shared. Most countries which, unlike Japan, can only cater for little beyond the domestic market, will find that the number of jobs decreases as computerization increases.

Terrorism

A new kind of terrorism using sophisticated technology is possible, especially in the field of nuclear technology. The chairman of the UK Atomic Energy Agency, Sir John Hill, acknowledged that there are literally dozens of books, periodicals, and unclassified publications available which contain information on the construction of nuclear weapons and nuclear plants. In 1972, a leaflet appeared in London entitled 'Towards a People's Bomb' which purported to describe how plutonium could be extracted and a crude nuclear weapon made by agencies other than governments. The claim was viewed with the greatest sceptism, but since then there have been confirmations from many sources of the availability outside governments of the know-how for the construction of a crude nuclear device. With information publicly available, students have been known to put together workable blueprints for such a device, the best known instance being the effort of an MIT undergraduate commissioned for this purpose by a television company.

The weakness of international control mechanisms, the hundreds of unescorted transports of nuclear material, unpoliced dumping grounds for nuclear waste, unstable governments in many countries with nuclear reactors, and the growth of international terrorism add to the possibility of terrorists using nuclear technology.

The most recent information on terrorist organizations is not only that they operate world-wide, but that they often have links with each other, exchanging information and arms. In this context, a weakly guarded nuclear reactor anywhere on the globe or a weakly guarded convoy of nuclear waste being moved out for disposal is an invitation for terrorists.

In April 1979, the Australian government viewed the proliferation of knowledge on nuclear weaponry so seriously
that it banned the publication and circulation of a book on
the making of a nuclear device.

The British Royal Commission on Environmental Pollution in 1976 drew attention to the possible impact of
nuclear terrorism on personal liberty. The commission
thought it remarkable that none of the official documents
produced so far had conveyed any unease on this score and
that nowhere was there any suggestion of apprehension
about the possible long-term dangers.

The legal consequences which can follow are intensified
surveillance of the nuclear workforce, suspension of *habeas
corpus* and of all provisions relating to freedom from arrest
and freedom from search, wide powers of interrogation by
the police and the military, the tapping of all telephone calls
and the scrutinizing of all mail, the prohibition of free movement, wholesale evacuation of populations from target areas,
suspension of international travel, suspension of press and
broadcasting freedom to check panic, the calling out of the
military, the freezing of food stocks and the enactment of
anti-hoarding laws.

The extreme risk involved in atomic power has resulted
in legislation which confers, in time of peace, power which
has hitherto been justified only under conditions of war or
emergency. The British Atomic Energy Authority's Special
Constabulary is an armed constabulary with power to arrest
on suspicion. In Australia, the *Atomic Energy Act* of 1953 –
a piece of defence legislation dating from the Cold War –
makes a person liable to a heavy fine or a prison sentence
for hindering or obstructing uranium mining. Search and
arrest are permissible without warrant; and the government
and the Atomic Energy Commission are immune from proceedings arising from wrongful arrest, detention and search.
The act is not a dead letter. In 1978, it was the subject of
amendment, which did not reduce these powers.

Military Intervention

There are dangers in involving the military in emergencies.
A bomb blast at the Sydney Hilton Hotel in February 1978,

at a regional meeting of Commonwealth Heads of Government, resulted in the Australian military force being used by a decision of the Executive Council. The council's minute stated that the governor-general was satisfied that because of terrorist activities and related violence in New South Wales it was necessary to call out the defence forces – one of the few instances in which the military forces have been used to support civil authorities in Australian peacetime history.

Many countries have natural disaster organizations to deal with sudden dislocations brought about by natural disasters, such as earthquakes and cyclones. The Victorian bushfires of February 1983 saw the military called out in their hundreds to help the civilian fire-fighting authorities. But such a situation is not fraught with the same constitutional and legal dangers as the use of military forces to curb terrorism, for the natural disaster organization would always be under the control of the civilian authority.

Martial law is another danger resulting from widespread terrorism. When army authorities are brought in to restore law and order, there is the danger that they will over-step their authority. The greater the threat, the greater the danger.

The fears induced by technological terrorism pale into insignificance when compared with fears of nuclear war.

Ever since the explosion of the world's first nuclear device, we have lived with the realization that the human race, or a substantial part of it, is capable of being instantly annihilated. The intervening period has only reinforced these fears, for time and again the world has been on the brink of nuclear war. The Cuban missile crisis is perhaps the best known. Prestigious institutions, such as the Swedish Institute of Peace Research, have issued warnings, on the basis of the most careful and objective calculations, that a nuclear catastrophe within the next decade is nearly a certainty unless there are drastic changes in world attitudes.

The threat manifests itself in disillusionment with the social order, distrust of institutions, the erosion of inherited value systems, and a disregard of long-term perspectives.

Occasional attempts to break this malaise of spirit are visible in the protests at rearmament and nuclear proliferation, now gathering momentum. Protests at the pursuit of the technological-materialistic way of life that led us to our present impasse took the form of the new left movement, the search for simpler ways of living and the quest for nontraditional spiritual values.

An Ageing Population

Through its beneficial work in the prolongation of human life, technology has created a social problem of another sort. The increasing proportion of the elderly in the population has been described as a quietly ticking social time bomb which will explode in twenty years.[25]

In Australia, as elsewhere, the proportion of the aged is visibly increasing. According to the 1982 edition of the Year Book, the proportion of the population aged sixty-five and above in Australia has risen from 8.43 per cent in 1971 to 9.59 per cent in 1980. At these rates of increase, considerable shifts can be expected in economics, welfare and politics over the next decade. Continuing inflation can wear down the value of the pensions or savings of the retired elderly. Health and social services will bear a new burden. The proportionately reduced working force, supporting a proportionately increased dependent group, may need to tighten belts and to be appeased by hand-outs. The new strain upon economies may result in grave political tensions if it means a cut in benefits.

A politically powerful group of elderly may not be prepared to change. Themselves the victims of bewildering change, they will tend to clutch at the values they feel they understand. An age which may need to see the drastic refashioning of its economic machinery may be unable to make obviously needed changes.

The United Nations General Assembly, recognizing this problem, convened a World Assembly on the Elderly in 1982 in Vienna from 26 July to 6 August 1982, which was intended to act as 'a forum to launch an international action programme aimed at guaranteeing economic and social security to older people as well as opportunities to contribute to national development'.

Unless appropriate policies are introduced, an increasing number of older people will be denied their basic human rights, lacking both participation in and contribution to their society, and developing a feeling of dependence on it.

Towards a Participatory Future

Society has benefited in many ways from science. Some of the very technologies whose dangers have been described, however, are capable of being turned into valuable tools for society.

The computer brings us closer to the Athenian participatory democracy model than any other voting device or procedure we have seen so far. It is now possible for a government wanting instant responses from people on any issue to obtain it by hooking up the home to a central computer. The millions now spent on referendums could be drastically reduced, costly postal vote procedures could be eliminated, and stationery and printing costs eliminated.

If instant voting is thus available, there will also be a greater tendency to submit issues to a direct vote rather than to resort, as is currently the case, to representative or collegiate voting devices. Electoral procedures will be streamlined, and there will be a move towards electoral systems based on the one person, one vote principle. One possible method is West Germany's 'ORAKEL', which combines electronic opinion polls with television discussions. A panel of thirty representative members of the general public, all on telephone lines, can join in the discussion at any time, while a group of experts in the studio supplies information whenever necessary on any factual matters raised. After the debate, arrangements are made for viewers to send in their responses.

The instant electronic vote has many other repercussions. The election of governments for a period of years is a device that has been resorted to largely owing to the expense and difficulty of general elections. Consequently, a government is voted into office and given the power to remain in office despite opinion in the electorate moving dramatically away from it at various periods during its office.

With the possibility of instant electronic polls at practically no expense to the state, this picture changes. Indeed, there could be a demand, if a definite and sustained swing is registered away from the government, for a change of government well ahead of the period set for its life. Governments will be kept on their toes, and there will be no smokescreens thrown over the true state of government popularity.

There will also be little or no time lag between dissolutions and elections, no delaying of issues until the will of the people becomes known. New constitutional principles may emerge requiring governments defeated on three successive national votes to resign, or requiring that, at the request of a certain percentage of the population, a popularity poll be taken.

This could engender a feeling of immediacy in the affairs of government. But it could also lead to an increasing apathy born of the confidence that consultation with the public is always available. It could lead to hasty and ill-considered public decisions if the procedure were resorted to too often. It would not be applicable to problems which do not have a yes/no answer. These aspects need to be watched.

There are many political functions the computer can perform other than linking citizens to a centre or to each other. It can also ensure that candidates will be held to their electoral promises. With computerization, the election statements of all candidates can be fed into a data bank for instant retrieval. A citizen wanting to know in 1983 what a candidate said on an issue in 1977 will have the means to put this information on a screen at home.

The computer could also reverse the trend towards uniformity by enabling those with similar interests to group together. There are large numbers of people with common interests who have thus far been prevented from pooling their resources and knowledge by lack of the means of communication. The instant communication available through the use of the computer will break down this isolation and promote the cohesion of these people into interest groups in a way that was not possible before.

Moving from the political to the social, we can expect profound implications to follow from the 'wired city', in which homes, offices, government agencies and data banks are all wired into each other. It is perhaps only twenty years away. There are many hopeful implications: urban concentration will be decentralized, individual participation in the decision-making process will be increased, travel time will be available for leisure and study, and the accountability of politicians and governments will increase. We may also be freed from dependence on the media for news.

Travel between home and office to a large extent will be eliminated, for decision making, conferences and even routine office work can than be done from the home. 'On demand' audio-visual retrieval of information displayed on the home television set would take care of shopping expeditions, catalogue searching, share quotations, financial information, and news. Two-way audio-visual communication between people or between people and machines will take care of financial planning, adult education, and a good part of secondary education.

These changes will alter the profiles of the office, the business firm, the home, the university, the school and the factory. Worker mobility will no longer be as essential as before. There may be neighbourhood remote work centres within walking distance of employees' homes, where a series of work spaces would be provided that were equipped with a bank of audio-visual communication services. Work spaces could be rented and would resemble a student carrel. Before the turn of the century, more than 90 per cent of the workforce in developed countries could be working from their homes or from neighbourhood remote work centres.[26]

Similar beneficial uses will be found for many other technologies, but legal and human rights groups of the future will need to be as vigilant about them as about the dangers of technology.

Chapter 6
The Human Habitat

Science and technology have significantly improved our ability to enjoy what the earth affords. A beneficent science continually brings within our grasp what was elusive before. Yet it also destroys what it gives because its power is so great that it enables people to consume the earth's resources, and already much irreversible damage has occurred. Our generation is drawing on resources that belong to all the generations which will follow us. If there is a human right to the enjoyment of the earth and what it offers, we are depriving our children and their children of it.

Many other human rights flow from it. Among them are the right to a healthy environment, the right to aesthetic and recreational enjoyment, the right to participation in the earth's resources, and the right to sustenance.

To support these rights, new principles of trusteeship and limited ownership of the earth's resources are evolving, as is the concept of community ownership of property. Procedural machinery, such as a world environmental fund, and schemes to improve the environment are planned. A common law of the environment is being spoken of as an important global legal concern.

Aesthetic and Recreational Enjoyment
The aesthetic enjoyment of nature and the recreational use of the earth, two natural rights which children and adults of all generations have enjoyed, are under threat. Technology,. from bullets to bulldozers, will exacerbate the ravages on fauna and flora and on the forests, and its other effects are seen after oil spills, in urban squalor, and in the effects of mining.

Fauna and Flora

In 1932, Australia launched its emu war when a machine-gun detachment was despatched complete with a military photographer to eradicate 20,000 emus in Western Australia. The emus miraculously escaped eradication.[1] The lyre bird, once plentiful, is scarcely to be seen, and many marsupials – the freckled marsupial mouse, Gaimard's rat-kangaroo, the broad-faced rat kangaroo, the brown hare-wallaby, Gilbert's rat-kangaroo – are lost for ever.

The story is the same the world over. The mammals, marsupials, birds, reptiles, trees, plants, ferns, shrubs are yearly losing members of their species.

Statistics of endangered species make frightening reading. According to the World Wildlife Fund, 345 bird species and 200 mammal species are threatened with extinction. In the last century, seventy-five bird species and twenty-seven mammal species disappeared; and fifty-three bird species and sixty-eight mammal species have already disappeared in this century. Plant life species now threatened with extinction number 20,000 to 25,000.

Forests

Forests are one of our steadily diminishing resources. They are being burned or cut at the rate of 20 hectares a minute. In addition, our tree population is dying annually by the hundreds of thousands as a result of detergents, rubbish dumping, fertilizers, and defoliants. On a world scale, half the forests have been felled since 1950.

Woodchip projects in Australia, conducted with high-grade technology, are spreading the dangerous cinnamon fungus root rot disease by altering drainage patterns and providing extensive roading on which vehicles carry the fungus to healthy areas. The fungus, described as 'unquestionably the most destructive plant pathogen (disease) ever recorded in native vegetation of this and possibly any region', is already a major problem in Western Australia, where more than 100,000 hectares of forests, mostly jarrah, are dead or dying, and it has infected between 300,000 and 400,000 hecatres of coastal forests in Victoria.[2]

In the world's rain forests alone there are an estimated

three million plants and organisms. Only 500,000 of them have been named. Of the 2,500,000 yet to be seen or named, many thousands will vanish before scientists identify them or get to know them or establish their potential use for humans. Plants and organisms as yet undiscovered could make a great contribution to our food and medical supplies, but 20,000 to 25,000 plant species will die out by the turn of the century.

Forests absorb some of the carbon dioxide concentration in the atmosphere caused by burning fossil fuels. As they disappear, the carbon dioxide levels rise. The balance is upset.

The greenhouse effect caused by the surplus carbon dioxide traps heat within the atmosphere and keeps warming up the globe.

The loss of tree cover contributes to erosion. A report commissioned by the US president, and released in 1980, revealed that the loss of tree cover resulted in a loss through erosion of an estimated 75,000,000,000 tonnes of topsoil around the world in the past seventy-five years. The dust clouds that moved across Melbourne in February 1983 were estimated to carry as much as 100,000 tonnes of topsoil and to have deposited around 10 kilograms of soil and mud on every suburban lot.

The clearing of the forests also raises the water table, for its deep roots no longer suck out the water to be pumped into the atmosphere. As water collects and the water table rises, it carries its salt layer to the surface, and green belts turn to arid wastes.

Urban Squalor

Twentieth-century cities have become the junkyard of technological civilization. The concrete jungle which is the habitat of a substantial proportion of the earth's population (and, with the drift to the cities, will be the habitat of substantially more) is compounded in its lack of aesthetic appeal by strewn garbage, junk and litter, garbage dumps, offensive odours, and rodents.

Cities, in time, will be buried under their own refuse, as New York's Environment Protection Administration said in

1970 of New York's annual accumulation of seven million tonnes of waste.[3]

Even where new suburbs have been built they are so unimaginative as to be no more than vast and ugly dormitory cities – row upon row of box-like houses supplied with water, electricity, sewerage and nothing else. In Sydney, Green Valley and Mount Druitt are examples. A former prime minister, Mr Gough Whitlam, once said of them, 'A Green Valley or a Mount Druitt is built not because the intentions of the sponsors are wicked but because the consequences are fully understood neither by the planners nor by the public.'[4]

Resource recovery acts, national materials policies, bureaus of solid waste management, a department of resources, indeed, a whole new systems approach is needed to solve this problem.

Mining and Power

Technology's search for energy has created an aesthetic blight. Surface mining is one of the worst offenders. Before the US became aware of the damage, 1.5 million hectares had been stripped, of which only half a million had been restored.[5] The requirements of reclamation reduced the damage, but vast recreational areas and wildlife habitats have been destroyed.

In Australia, the mining of rutile, ilmenite and zircon in beaches and sands has resulted in the complete removal of vegetation and the flattening of sandhills. Although the bulldozed remains in large areas can be carefully replanted, the natural state cannot be regained, and natural communities which have existed for thousands of years are gone for ever – as in the Myall Lakes area in New South Wales.[6]

Many industrialized countries have subsequently introduced reclamation legislation where open mining is in operation. Yet there are many areas which reclamation legislation will never reach.

Much of the land surface of the Republic of Nauru, for example, resembles in its pock-marked character a moonscape of gaping craters. The phosphates were dug out, and the company which mined them was not obliged to restore the land and made ghost quarries of the island. On Ocean Island, another Pacific Island which became a British settlement in 1900, the crown granted a British company exclusive rights to mine phosphate. The land was worked in such a fashion that extensive levelling and engineering operations as well as massive importation of soil was required to restore the land. The islanders recently failed in an action by them against the British Phosphate Commissioners for an order requiring the latter to restore and replant the worked out land.[7] The case proved to be one of the most prolonged and complex pieces of litigation in UK legal history.

Deep coal mining is also not environmentally harmless. An unpublished manuscript of the US Bureau of Mines estimated in 1971 that of three million hectares undermined by deep coal mines, over one million hectares had already subsided.[8] Millions more hectares will be undermined between now and the twenty-first century. Landscapes littered with millions of tonnes of mining debris in all the major mining countries are a major contributor to their dreary landscapes, and power cables are another source of aesthetic pollution.

Oil Spills
Dr Thor Heyerdahl, author of *The Kon Tiki Expedition*, reported that during his first attempt to cross the Atlantic on his raft in 1969, the water surface was free from tarry blobs and oil globules on only a few days out of two months.[9]

Oil spills both destroy recreational uses of beaches and damage the aquatic environment. On a pebbly beach, the oil may penetrate the stones in a manner which makes it difficult to dislodge, while on a sandy beach it may be buried under layers of fresh sand. This process may be repeated, so that an apparently clean beach is in reality badly polluted, and the pollution exposed during later storms. Massive oil spills, such as the Torrey Canyon disaster in 1967, when an oil tanker ran aground off the south coast of England, occur with monotonous regularity.

Oil spillage forms blanket surfaces over water and inhibits the respiration and feeding of small animals. Some smaller animals become weighted down by clinging oil and are carried to their destruction by waves and currents. Small seaweeds become similarly encrusted and torn away by waves. A variety of hydrocarbons can enter the leaves and stems of plants or the delicate skin covering fish gills and adversely affect their health. In addition, spilt oil may affect the whole structure of natural communities by tilting balances which have developed in response to long-established environmental pressures. Crude oils in water have produced deformities and death in herring larvae, and adult fish have been killed in large numbers after oil spills. The sea, as a result, is rapidly ceasing to be aesthetically and recreationally enjoyable.

The Right to Sustenance

Erosion, thermal pollution, acid rain, the break-down of the ultra-violet shield and the greenhouse effect are destroying life-support systems and impinging on our rights.

Erosion

The layer of soil in which most of our food is grown is fast deteriorating through 'anthropogenic' erosion, that is, erosion set off by people: heavy machinery used on farms and for urban construction diminishes the infiltration capacity of the soil by compacting it, thus resulting in more erosion as water accumulates on the surface; vast machine planted crops give the soil little protection against rain and cause accelerated surface run off; deforestation exposes humus covered soil the richness of which is rapidly washed away. As industrialization and technology progress, mining, waste disposal, cable construction and roadways will increase the extent of erosion.

The fine soil particles detached by surface erosion block up irrigation and drainage canals, raising the level of river beds and causing floods; and they raise the groundwater level, causing waterlogging. The capacity of water reservoirs can be silted by as much as 33 per cent within fifty years of their construction,[10] which produces a decline in the volume of water available for power production.

Dust bowls and dust storms are another result, as virgin land gradually yields to industrialization, and as farming becomes mechanized. Deprivations of human rights from the conversion of fertile lands into dustbowls are graphically captured in John Steinbeck's novel, *Grapes of Wrath*: lack of employment, starvation, the break-up of families, mass migration, eviction, suicide and death. The fine dust particles also cause serious lung disease.

The catalogue of damage is not complete without reference to the transportation of chemical substances by erosion. Chemicals of various levels of toxicity infiltrate surface and groundwaters, affecting the quality of water resources. Fertilizers, pesticides, herbicides, and fungicides are transported with the dust over enormous distances: wind-blown Sahara dust, for example, has been found in West Germany and Britain, and effluent discharged from Australia's eastern seaboard affects the Great Barrier Reef.[11]

Pesticides are often so persistent that even twenty years after their application 40 per cent remain in the soil.[12] Certain insecticides are highly persistent and, like DDT, accumulate in living bodies. When the bonds between organic and metallic substances, such as those between mercury and inorganic salts, break down, the inorganic substances accumulate, resulting in death. This was illustrated in mercury poisonings in Japan in 1953-60, caused by fish ingesting chemicals from pesticides which had found their way into the sea.

National and international research and efforts at erosion control supported by economic and impact evaluations will be an important future activity.

Thermal Pollution
The delicately maintained temperature balance in the world's water systems is essential to aquatic life. As this balance is progressively upset, an important source of food is threatened. Heated water from industry is discharged into rivers, lakes and the sea, raising the temperature by ten or twenty degrees. Thermal pollution has taken place: insects, prompted by the artificially heated water, emerge to mate too early in the spring; the fish spawning cycle, heavily dependent on temperature changes, is upset; the oxygen content of water is affected; and all levels of marine and aquatic life are endangered in the vicinity of the pollution.

As energy consumption increases so does the problem of thermal pollution. Species with a narrow tolerance range of temperature differences are the first to be affected. A difference of a few degrees, for example, can kill a fish. Migratory fish, guided often by water temperatures to their traditional streams, may run off course to destruction.

An interesting by-product of the increase in energy consumption, referred to in a recent report of the National Research Council in the US, is that in the next fifty to seventy-five years, the temperature rise could raise water levels so high that New York City and Los Angeles would have to be evacuated.[13]

The release of heat into the atmosphere through the burning of fossil fuels or the creation of nuclear energy is another form of thermal pollution. Weather and climatic variations resulting from atmospheric heat pollution can also destroy the delicately balanced cycles on which various forms of plant and animal life depend.

Acid Rain

Acid rain results from chemical emissions from metal smelting and fossil fuel combustion and threatens food resources, both aquatic and agricultural. What is more, chemicals generated in one country may be deposited as acid rain in another, raising some political and legal questions: for example, Norway and Sweden are adversely affected by European countries, Canada by the US, and neighbouring Asian countries by Japan.

The ecological effects are severe. In southern Sweden, it has been estimated that fish populations in more than 15,000 lakes have been affected by acid precipitation; in Norway, acidification of thousands of fresh water lakes and streams has affected fish population in an area of 20,000 square kilometres.[14] Acid precipitation also leaches nutrients from foliage and minerals from the soil, erodes surfaces, and inhibits nitrogen fixation.

International action is called for in view of the clear scientific demonstrations that it is not necessarily the polluting country that suffers. The polluter's garbage, literally dumped in a neighbour's backyard, thus affects the rights of millions of underprivileged people, whose marginal food supplies cannot be diminished without loss of life. The total national cost in reduced crop and fish production, dwindling forests, and structural damage is impossible to assess.

The Ultra-Violet Shield

The vital ozone layer in the stratosphere is being destroyed by technology ranging from aerosol sprays to supersonic transport. This layer, known as the ozonosphere, effectively blocks dangerous solar radiation from reaching the earth's surface, and is important for the existence of life.

Although there has been no substantial rise in the production of fluorocarbons from aerosol spray cans in the past five years, there has been an increase in the use of the chemical Freon F-22 in refrigeration and of methyl chloroform in solvents. Both these chemicals add to the volume of stratospheric chlorine, a chemical which reduces ozone amounts.[15]

There is a widespread fear that the ozone shield will also be disturbed by the flight of increasing numbers of supersonic aeroplanes.[16] Some estimates place the fleet of supersonic jets that will be flying by 1985 at 500, each of which every hour will consume 66 tonnes of carbon dioxide, 3 tonnes of carbon monoxide and 3 tonnes of nitric oxide.[17] In the dry stratosphere, these massive injections of foreign material could set in motion a series of chemical reactions which would further deplete the ozone layer. Pollutants released into the stratosphere are not swept away but keep accumulating, with resulting increases in concentration, making it specially vulnerable to intrusions such as supersonic jets.

The Greenhouse Effect

The accumulation of carbon dioxide in the atmosphere tends to trap heat on the earth's surface, thus producing the greenhouse effect.

Observations made at a number of background measuring stations around the world have shown that the carbon dioxide concentration in the atmosphere is increasing at the rate of 0.4 per cent per year.[18] At present rates of increase of fossil fuel consumption, carbon dioxide levels in the atmosphere will increase seven-fold during the next fifty years. This could affect the distribution of rainfall and create deserts of much of the grain-producing areas of the northern hemisphere.

The Right to Health

Human rights have been widened to take in this concept, which includes the right to health, free from dangers brought by new technology.

Chemical Dangers

In December 1976, traces of a highly toxic chemical were found in thousands of people in Michigan: polybrominated biphenyl had been mixed accidentally with animal food and delivered to hundreds of Michigan farms. Large quantities of infected meat, milk and eggs had been sold throughout the state, and hundreds of people became sick.

Accident is not the only danger of the chemicals explosion, which started in the 1940s and 1950s. Lethal chemicals have been deliberately pushed into the environment.

Over 70,000 chemicals are in worldwide commercial use. Another 1,000, the side-effects of which have not been tested, come on the market each year. Until 1976, when the US and some other countries enacted legislation, such as the *Toxic Substances Control Act*, the requirement to test substances before they were released was almost non-existent.

The World Health Organization estimates that 75 to 85 per cent of all cancers are triggered by environmental agents, such as industrial chemicals. Some of these chemicals require twenty to forty years to produce tumours, and nearly all of them are less than forty years old.

The phenoxy-herbicides 2,4,5-T and 2,4-D are suspected of producing cancers, and Agent Orange, sprayed in the Vietnam jungles, has caused cancer, sterility and deformities in Vietnam veterans.

Often it is a chance factor that alerts us to the danger. An epidemic of an extremely rare cancer of the liver was found, for example, in workers in the plastics industry in the early

1970s. The cancers were first linked with direct exposure to vinyl chloride, the key chemical in the plastics industry. Later it was realized that workers making thousands of derivative products were also affected. The culprit chemical was probably discovered because the disease it caused was rare. Had it produced a common disease, such as lung cancer, it might have remained undetected. Apart from its use in plastics, vinyl chloride is used as an aerosol propellant in hair sprays, and in insecticides and room deodorants, often accumulating indoors after less than a minute's spraying.

Diseases caused by chemicals kill several hundred thousand workers each year. Among the worst offenders are asbestos, fibreglass and kepone.

Legal regulation of the danger is impossible, for neither legal nor laboratory machinery can tell us before a chemical is released whether it will produce a lethal effect in twenty to forty years. The chemicals industry argues that the health hazards resulting from these chemicals are part of the price we must pay for the benefits that chemical products bring. The chemical lobby is a powerful one and exerts much influence on government and occupational health and safety boards. Indeed, the US National Institute of Occupation Safety and Health (NIOSH) failed initially to notify twenty-one million workers known to have been exposed to material dangerous to their health. At a 1977 Senate hearing, NIOSH officials estimated that it would cost $35 a person to find and notify the twenty-one million workers involved and that keeping them under medical observation alone would cost $5,000 million. Whether the government should find the funds is one of the issues of debate.

If there is substance in the contention that the environment is being cumulatively poisoned by chemicals – a little in the deodorant and in the hair dye, a little on the skin of the apple, a little in the household paint and in the drinking water – we may by slow degrees be poisoning our health or damaging succeeding generations through genetic deformities.

The real problem lies, however, in the unexpected side-effects and the proliferation of untested chemicals. It has taken us forty years of study and thousands of scientific papers to understand DDT, for example, which has not as yet been completely assessed. It has been estimated that 30,000 to 40,000 scientific papers have been written about 2,4,5-T. As we have 40,000 types of insecticides, fungicides, and herbicides, of which 750 million kilograms are used each year, the task of scientific testing is beyond our means.

A dramatic confirmation of some of the fears expressed in this chapter made international headlines on 24 February 1983. The Reagan administration announced that it would buy out all 2,400 residents of Times Beach, Missouri, after confirming that the town was too contaminated with the toxic compund dioxin to be safe for habitation. The Environmental Protection Agency therefore decided to buy the entire town after learning that dioxin levels were 300 times those considered to be safe. Dioxin, the generic name for 75 compounds formed by unwanted byproducts in the manufacture of certain herbicides, has caused cancer and birth defects in animals and is believed to be lethal to humans. Residents were embittered that the government had known about the problem for ten years, but that the EPA had created loopholes in the law, allowing its unrestricted use. It was also significant that Times Beach was only one of 418 contaminated areas around the country that were priorities for being cleaned up under a $1,600 million fund established to clean up the nation's most hazardous waste dumps.

Recombinant DNA Experiments
In 1956 two researchers, Francis Crick and James Watson, published an article in *Nature* explaining the structure of the DNA molecule (deoxyribonucleic acid). These long thread-like molecules contain encoded genetic information for the building of the life form of which that molecule was the base. This discovery of the building blocks on which all life forms are constructed was as momentous in scientific history as the splitting of the atom. Its discovery has given us the ability to splice and reassemble pieces of this long molecule. By doing so we can construct a life form which has never existed before.

When scientists first undertook recombinant DNA experiments, there was a fear that they might produce a bacterium, which if it escaped from the laboratory could endanger humans, just as myxomatosis wiped out rabbits in Australia. These fears were first raised by the Australian scientist, Sir McFarlane Burnet, and led in time to a scientific moratorium on recombinant DNA experiments. Subsequent experience has shown that these fears were largely unjustified, but until then national guidelines were issued in the US and elsewhere, to guard against the anticipated dangers.

The development and marketing of new genetically altered organisms, plants, and animals has become big business. In the US, the cultivation of micro-organisms in food processing, and the fermentation of wines and spirits is worth 88 thousand million dollars.[19] These established industries, however, will be revamped by genetic engineering, which will also create new industries. In industrial microbiology, for example, the new technology will not only improve the performance of bacteria yeasts and moulds but also create new organisms which will bring major changes to agriculture, forestry, and medicine. Genetic engineering may even create enzymes which have unforeseen reactions.[20]

Commercial interests will not readily submit to controls. When pharmaceutical companies in the US saw profit in continuing with research for the highly profitable manufacture of insulin, they publicly announced that they would not consider themselves bound by National Institute of Health guidelines because they did not depend on its funding.

Uncontrolled experimentation, where profit is the motive, needs to be monitored. To rely on the inherent good sense of the scientific community assumes that it is aware of and capable of judging the ethical issues involved. Lawyers, lay people, ethicists, and theologians must be involved.

Noise Pollution

People in industrialized countries take pride in scientific advances that make life more comfortable. Some, however, produce a substantial rise in noise levels.

Since the 1970s, there has been a growing awareness of the dangers of noise pollution. On 31 December 1970, the US president directed the Environmental Protection Agency to conduct a full investigation of noise and its effect on public health and welfare.

Exposure to noise can damage the inner ear, resulting in temporary or permanent hearing loss (noise levels of 70 to 80 decibels), interference with communication, and disturbance of sleep, relaxation, and concentration. Permanent damage can also occur to factory workers exposed to continuous noise.

Apart from the physiological and psychological effects on humans, noise has adverse effects on animals and buildings. The body's startled response to sudden sound, such as the sonic boom, produces changes in hormone levels, blood composition and other biochemical and physiological effects.[21] In animals, high sound levels have been found to interfere with reproductive functions. We are not fully aware how humans react, although cardiovascular diseases, ear, nose, and throat disorders, and equilibrium disorders appear to have a higher incidence than normal among workers exposed to high levels of noise. Headache and nervousness are also associated with noise pollution. There is some evidence that admissions to psychiatric hospitals are higher in areas with high noise levels than in quieter areas, although this is not entirely proved.

Nuclear Energy
The proliferation of nuclear reactors, leakages from a number of them, and the possibilities of major accidents threaten our survival.

The problem of the disposal of nuclear waste raises the question to what extent can this generation leave to its successors an environment, which, through the dumping of wastes, whether in salt beds, the depths of the oceans or deep trenches, is unsafe.

It is said that a safe means of disposal will be found, or alternatively that we are on the verge of a breakthrough which will give us clean nuclear energy. Until such time, the impossibility of safe disposal must provide the factual basis for discussion.

The human right to special care for motherhood and childhood stands violated by the threat of nuclear energy, for scientists tell us that radiation causes genetic mutations and an increased likelihood of producing defective offspring. Radiation can also result in seriously deformed offspring through chromosomal damage to sperm or eggs, and foetuses can be damaged in the first three months of pregnancy through injury to specific cells which develop into deformed limbs or internal organs. Such damage increases with the intensity of exposure. Furthermore, radioactivity in the environment tends to collect in such foods as milk, with resulting damage to children.

If the residents of a city were exposed to radioactive contamination through a serious nuclear accident, they would run the risk of producing defective offspring. National interest may demand their compulsory sterilization to prevent a large number of defective children putting a strain on community resources. We are only a nuclear accident away from this.

Workers in the nuclear industry, whether in the mines, the reactors, or the transport of wastes, are exposed to dangerous levels of radiation. In the UK, the heirs of two nuclear power workers at Windscale were awarded compensation in 1982 for developing cancer as a result of their work. This was the first admission in court in the UK that radiation exposure among plutonium workers had led to cancer. It is difficult in these cases to establish legally the link between a particular cancer and the worker's service at a nuclear power plant, because the cancer may not manifest itself for twenty or thirty years after the worker's initial exposure to radiation. Laws imposing time limits on legal actions raise a legal difficulty, for a traditional principle of the law holds that the right of action is lost if it is delayed too long. A report published by the National Radiological Protection Board in February 1983 admitted that another seven people may have died through cancers or suffered hereditary defects from the effects of the 1957 Windscale fire. This accident had led to radioactive iodine being released into the atmosphere, after which winds spread the radioactive cloud over England, Wales and parts of northern Europe.

No insurance mechanisms in the world can adequately compensate people who suffer as a result of a reactor accident. Legislation, such as the *Price Anderson Act* in the US, has sought to limit compensation to $560 million a reactor. Actions filed by groups of affected people as a result of the Harrisburg leak run to over a thousand million dollars and cover a variety of claims, including damage to health and property, loss of employment, and damages for evacuation.

The most recent estimate by the Nuclear Regulatory Commission (NRC) released in November 1982 surpasses earlier estimates of death and property damage from reactor accidents. The 1975 NRC estimate of $14,000 million property damage has been raised in the 1982 figures to over $300,000 million in certain areas such as New York City, and the number of early deaths from 3,000 to over 100,000.

The events in Harrisburg have demonstrated how close we could be to a nuclear accident. Nuclear reactors are proliferating, and legal powers of the International Atomic Agency within national boundaries are inadequate, for problems arise of infringement of sovereignty. The risks of a nuclear accident in the next ten years are high.

In the US, by the end of the century, there is an almost 2 per cent chance of a nuclear accident. When all the world's nuclear reactors, some of them poorly managed, are taken into account, there is a 5-10 per cent chance of such an accident by the end of the century.

An index of world attitudes towards the dangers of nuclear energy was the plebiscite conducted in February 1983 in the Republic of Palau, a US trust territory in the Western Pacific. The US was offering $1,200 million in aid and recognition of autonomy, in return for the option of placing nuclear materials in Palau, for transit or overflight purposes or for 'military necessity as determined by the government of the US'. Conscious of the radiation illness suffered by the neighbouring Kwajalein and Bikini Islanders for thirty years as a result of bomb and missile testing, the Palauans rejected the dazzling offer.

Space Pollution
There is a great deal of radioactive material already contaminating outer space, which, if not already a part of the human

environment, is becoming increasingly important to it.

The Russian satellite Cosmos 954 which crashed over Canada, resulted in a ten-month long search for radioactive debris. In October 1978, the Canadian government ended this search after recovering 3,000 pieces from the frozen wastes of the north. Some pieces contained no radioactivity at all, but others were reputed to be potent enough, in the view of the Atomic Energy Control Board, to kill within a few hours.

A nuclear reactor fuelled by uranium 235 had been installed in the satellite to support a satellite-borne radar system which needed large amounts of power. The Russians did not bargain for the accident, but the plan was that once the life of the satellite had ended, the reactor was to be detached and boosted to an altitude of 1,280 kilometres. At this altitude, the reactor would take 600 years to re-enter the earth's atmosphere but upon re-entry would cause pollution. We do not know how many similar satellites are in orbit and therefore do not have any control over their re-entry.

More recently, in August 1981, a former premier of Western Australia, Sir Charles Court, conscious of the fear and disruption caused by the crash of the US Skylab satellite in Western Australia, called for the establishment of an international agency to monitor all the fragments in space. He was prompted to do so by the news that the Soviet Cosmos 434 was reportedly entering the earth's atmosphere over Australia.[22]

The progress of science has enabled us to see environmental concerns beyond earth. Outer space will one day be part of our environment and, leaving aside responsibilities towards other forms of extra-terrestrial life, people's responsibilities to other people demand that space be protected from pollution. It is heartening that the office of space law of the United Nations is already concerned with and working on this problem.

The Right to Participate in the Earth's Resources

The earth being a common resource of all mankind, every inhabitant has as much right to its enjoyment as any other.

This principle, axiomatic though it may seem, is being constantly undermined by technology at the command of the industrialized nations. Nations lacking the technology are left out of their share.

The right to an equal share in the wealth of the sea is effectively negated by a technology which will help the developed nations to exhaust seabed resources before the developing nations can even reach them. The issues involved form a central issue of the current North-South debate.

There is also a time dimension to such concerns. The right to the earth's resources belongs not only to those who are now in existence. Countless future generations have as much right to these assets as the present population. Many Third World legal traditions, such as the African and the Melanesian, accord rights to future generations and treat them as members of the human family for whom those now alive are only trustees. They are as much entitled to non-renewable earth resources as anyone now alive.

Other fields in which these problems are surfacing are energy, minerals, and food resources.

The Sea
Traditionally, international law regarded the sea as a portion of the globe which anyone was free to use as he or she pleased. A new concept of the sea as a 'common heritage of mankind' is supported by the Geneva Convention on the High Seas, which points out that the seas should be used by states with regard to the interests of other states.

As a result, positive international controls have developed, such as the International Conventions for the Prevention of Pollution of the Seas by Oil (1954) and the International Convention on the Prevention of Pollution from Ships (1974). The fear of radiation pollution from nuclear-powered vessels has been dispelled, in part, by requirements set out in the International Convention for the Safety of Life at Sea.

The leading industrial nations regularly dump nuclear wastes in barrels by the thousand, as though they were leak-proof for 20,000 years. Between 1946 and 1970, the US dumped 86,758 containers containing low-level radioactive wastes in the sea, and by 1976 European countries had dumped 113,370 containers of radioactive wastes in the sea. It is estimated that other countries have dumped 45,970 tonnes of radioactive waste in the sea between 1967 and 1976.[23] Various countries, the US and UK included, also make elaborate plans for burying nuclear waste in the ocean bed, as though that gives any better assurance of safety. If and when the containers leak, the sea, a principal food resource, will be contaminated. Even if the wastes are discharged within territorial waters, it offends against a basic principle of international law that states should knowingly use their territory for acts contrary to the rights of other states. It is significant that radioactive substances are omitted from the scope of the Oslo Convention for the Prevention of Marine Pollution by Dumping from Ships and Aircraft (1972). The deliberate use of the sea as a dumping ground for wastes, including radioactive waste was a major issue at the UN Conference on the Human Environment held at Stockholm in 1972, but the international record so far is a sorry violation of many basic principles of the preservation of the seas.

In February 1983, a Spanish resolution calling for a moratorium on the dumping into the sea of radioactive waste was adopted by the Maritime Pollution Convention by nineteen votes to six. The resolution has no legal power but implies a moral obligation of the nations which voted. It urged suspension of dumping until scientists showed that dumping was not harmful to marine life. Significantly, the six nations which were not prepared to accept even a moral commitment, and voted against the resolution, included the US, Britain, Japan and South Africa. Japan made it clear that it would go ahead with plans to dump nuclear waste in the Pacific Ocean. This news was followed a few days later by the alarming news that the US Navy had chosen a lonely spot in the Pacific for the dumping of its ageing and obsolete nuclear submarines – an action which in the opinion of some scientists could lead to the irreversible spread of radioactivity into the food chain.

Nuclear weapons test explosions, which cause radioactive marine pollution, anywhere under water, both in territorial waters and on the high seas, was banned by the Nuclear Test Ban Treaty (1963), and a treaty of 1971 bans countries from putting nuclear weapons on the sea bed. The US and USSR deploy large fleets of nuclear-powered submarines all over the world, and an accident to any one of them could result in nuclear material being discharged into the oceans. Nuclear testing does not have to take place under water, however, to pollute the ocean. A test performed on an island can contaminate the seas around it. Indeed, the UN Group of Experts on the Scientific Aspects of Marine Pollution has stressed the importance of atmospheric transfer, pointing out that for many pollutants this is the principal pathway into the ocean. During the six months following the explosion of a number of nuclear bombs on Bikini Island in 1954, for example, radioactive fish were discarded in the sea in the Kuroshio current a distance of 5,000 kilometres away.[24]

The ocean's food resources are being similarly appropriated by those who command the necessary technology. The US, for example, takes thousands of tonnes of fish from the world's richest tuna grounds adjacent to Papua New Guinea, and its vast food reserves go into canneries in the US with no compensation to Papua New Guinea.

The sea is one of the most important of the earth's resources, both in its food and minerals. Technology is making the equal enjoyment of this common resource increasingly difficult.

Energy
Energy needs to be perceived not merely as an aspect of the free enterprise system but as a problem incorporating the major human rights issues of our time. The problem is no longer one of more energy production but of more energy conservation.

However clearly moral imperatives point against the use of nuclear energy, the dependence of the industrial nations on increasing energy supplies is so great that the strongest political and economic pressure will be mounted for its continuing use. Even organized labour, especially that in the construction, machinery and electrical trades, may favour nuclear power on the basis that it means more jobs.

An index of the political pressures generated by the problem was the opposition to President Carter's energy package in 1977. It was opposed in the Senate and was eventually accepted only with considerable modifications. Putting his finger on the human rights aspects involved, President Carter said, 'It is time for the public interest to prevail over special interest lobbyists.' [25] At every stage, whether in the conservation of energy or the switch to solar energy, special interest groups will stand four-square in the way of overall national policy.

Legal planning in the energy field must start with the prevention of waste. In the US, the Ford administration placed on the statute book energy conservation measures, such as efficiency labelling for appliances and gasoline efficiency standards for cars. These measures, useful in themselves, are only a beginning. An extraordinary percentage of energy, wastefully created, is wastefully used. The car, for example, uses less then 10 per cent of its fuel to make it move and less than 10 per cent of that power for personal transport. Thousands of cars, burning their own weight in fuel every year, still carry one person to and from work.[26] According to the American Physical Society, the thermodynamic efficiency of electric hot water systems is only 1.5 per cent and of space heating 8 per cent. Manufacturers of such appliances, often connected by shareholdings and common interests with the energy industry, have not been conspicuous in their attempts to assess the wastefulness of their products. Lawyers and legislators in association with technologists will need to draw up legislation to reduce such waste.

President Carter's comprehensive energy programme, with some important modifications, resulted in the *Energy Security Act* of 1980. This pioneering and carefully reasoned national legislative blueprint for the elimination of waste was set out in eight sections, each dealing with an area of special energy concern. Nearly all the major thrusts of the Carter energy package were neutralized in President Reagan's economic report to Congress on 18 February 1981, in which he dismantled regulations and sharply reduced federal involvement in the development of alternative energy sources.

As with waste prevention, preparation for the age of solar energy needs considered legal attention, especially in Australia, with its vast surface area. The maximum use of solar energy for the purpose of domestic consumption, for example, is an aspect to which the law relating to urban planning must direct its attention. Just as a certain amount of light and air has been made mandatory in the construction of new houses, so the maximum facilities for solar heating should be set as a precondition for the approval of new houses. Stipulations that every new house should have an auxiliary solar heating unit, and legal regulations against shading of space on adjacent premises may be needed. Zoning regulations will be needed to preserve the reception of sunlight by solar collectors, and town planning concepts will need to be revised. The relationship between electric and gas suppliers and solar energy suppliers will need to be regulated, and tax legislation will need to be restructured to give incentives to the harnessing of solar energy for industrial and domestic purposes.[27]

Electricity generated from solar energy may not perhaps be as economical as that obtained from nuclear energy. But the bare cost of production of nuclear energy by no means represents its cost to the community in human and human rights terms. If health and environmental factors are considered, they will inflate several hundred-fold the true cost of nuclear energy to the community.

It is ironical that although a plan aimed at putting a man on the moon could gear all national resources and energies to its accomplishment, the more pressing need for solving what remains of the solar energy problem can elicit no such response. The natural nuclear reactor we have in space is far enough away to be harmless. It consumes its own radioactive products and beams to us free of charge a thousand times the energy we will need. If the solar energy reaching 10 per cent of the Australian desert can be harnessed at 10 per cent efficiency, it can supply the world with power for ever.[28] It is extravagant to waste this resource.

The belief that more energy means more satisfaction of the right to employment needs to be examined. The nuclear energy lobby makes constant reference to the survival of energy-dependent western societies as requiring an ever-increasing supply of energy, the only adequate and economic source of which is said to be nuclear energy. An argument that seems to reinforce such contentions is that when the energy supply suddenly cuts out, such as during an industrial strike, thousands of people are thrown out of work. More energy does not necessarily mean more jobs, however, because not infrequently high technology means that fewer people are employed.

Unfortunately, anti-nuclear campaigners did not arm themselves adequately with information to counter the predictions, put out by the nuclear lobby, of economic chaos and loss of jobs in the absence of nuclear energy, and figures are only now being prepared.

Food

A recent book on world hunger[29] points out in its preface that if it takes the reader six hours to read the book, somewhere in the world, 2,500 people will have died of starvation or of a hunger-related illness before they turn the last page. By the turn of the century, the number could double. 'Food justice' is as important a human rights issue as any other.

The technology which produced 'miracle' strains of grain induced Third World farmers to rely on advanced technology for their seeds and fertilizers. Once this dependence was created, they lost their traditional ability to raise their own crops without assistance.

Patents in new seed varieties give their creators a financial interest which they do not hesitate to exploit, putting power in the hands of the technologically advanced countries. The new plant varieties developed by the plant technologists have led to a plant variety rights system which allows plant breeders to collect royalties from those who sell or use varieties developed by them and registered under the scheme. Most western countries have such schemes in operation, justifying them on the basis of the intensive work and expenditure involved in research. Current legislation gives the patent holders the sole rights to market the seed of the species they develop.

In countries which have passed such legislation, most of the small seed-producing companies have been taken over by multi-national corporations. Farmers' dependence on the patent-owning company is now complete: they must go to them again for fresh supplies because the seeds developed by these companies are not hardy enough to be re-used. In this way, the production cycles in many Third World countries have been broken.

Seed production technology and therefore agricultural power is now confined to a few companies, mainly producers of petro-chemical fertilizers and pesticides, such as Pfizer, Royal-Dutch Shell, Ciba-Geigy and Occidental Petroleum. There is at once a clash between the profit motive and the food needs, especially of the poor world, the food supply of which may now be largely controlled by outside financial interests. The withholding of seed supply can become a powerful political weapon.

The technology of agriculture also makes food a political weapon in the hands of a few surplus grain producers of the world: the US, Canada, and Australia. In a food shortage, these countries would be the arbiters of the distribution of the surplus until a world food distribution authority were evolved, free of political and profit-making motives.

Another aspect of world food patterns is the manner in which the worldwide power of agricultural technology is directing its effort into financially productive crops. Brazil, despite its desperately hungry millions, for example, has committed itself to an alcohol-fuel economy, ingesting millions of kilograms of sugar cane into its distilleries to produce ethanol and alcohol.[30] Fertilizer, which the starving Salel desperately needs for its own foods, is pumped into fields which grow proteins for the livestock industries of the developed world. In addition, many poorer countries have been persuaded to go in for capital-intensive mechanized farming and harvesting in place of their traditional farming methods.

Hunger cannot be isolated. We cannot reasonably expect 85 per cent of the population to look on peacefully while the affluent 15 per cent enjoy 85 per cent of the world's food and assets. Law and order will break down, not merely nationally but globally, with numerous human rights problems following in their train.[31]

Food thus provides the essential background to the

current picture of the human habitat. In the shaping of this background, technology has played an important role. In unwinding the current tensions, technology can likewise play an important role.

Minerals

The Australian scientist, Professor Charles Birch, in his seminal book, *Confronting the Future*, depicts modern man in the developed world as wrapped up in tonnes of steel, copper, aluminium, lead, tin, zinc and plastics, each day gobbling up 30 kilograms of raw steel and many kilograms of other minerals. To this we could add the image of each person using a barrel of oil every six days.[32]

The east coast of the US produces an average of 2 kilograms of garbage per person per day: about a tonne a person each year.[33] New York State's annual garbage contains 103,000 tonnes of aluminium (worth $30.9 million), 1.5 million tonnes of iron and steel (worth $60 million), 1.3 million tonnes of glass (worth $31.6 million), 885,800 tonnes of paper (worth $13.2 million), 41,200 tonnes of other non-ferrous metals (worth $18.5 million), and 12.3 million tonnes of fuel (worth $142 million).

We are all familiar with the forecasts of the periods within which resources of oil, tin, copper, lead, zinc and other basic requirements will run out. Such a run on the earth's resources, and the resulting extreme shortages which we shall experience by the turn of the century, will mean that many minerals and commodities will be strictly rationed. This will breed increasing governmental controls. Car permits, fuel permits, 'meat permits', 'garden permits' and even 'baby permits' will appear. The growth of such controls will in time provoke the emergence of totalitarianism. The trend will be towards military-socialist governments as the only regimes capable in this context of establishing social or economic systems of a workable nature.

Military Technology

A large proportion of the resources extracted from the earth is devoted to military technology, and more than half the world's technological manpower is channelled into the production of armaments. Armaments technology makes no attempt to conceal that its only purpose is to destroy human life. How much longer will it be legitimate under international and national law for scarce resources to be used for the destruction of humans and their habitat?

The armaments trade occupies an honoured place in legitimate international trade. While trade in drugs and narcotics is relentlessly tracked down by armies of police and customs officials, the arms trade has the blessings of governments. Powerful nations vie with each other to stage great arms fairs.

Nuclear Weapons

In 1981, President Reagan decided to spend $180.3 thousand million over the next six years on a massive campaign of nuclear weapons building. Several thousand new nuclear warheads were to be deployed by the US under the plan.

Plans to build a new generation of nuclear warheads in the 1980s necessitate the production of more bomb-grade plutonium than is currently available to the military. The result is that the military establishment is now looking at the possible use of spent fuel rods from commercial nuclear reactors.[34] Such a connection between the commercial nuclear industry and the military was taboo in the past, and the possibility of its happening provoked a storm of protest in the US and abroad and lent support to the fears that nuclear technology would eventually provide another powerful bridge between industry and the military.

India some years ago earned US and world censure for allegedly turning 'atoms for peace' into the production of 'atoms for war'. Such a strict separation also provided the rationale for the tripartite Treaty on the Non-Proliferation of Nuclear Weapons in 1968 by which the US, the UK and the USSR recognized the inalienable right of all parties to develop nuclear research for peaceful purposes. Today India has four operating nuclear power plants, and the US technical newsletter, *Nuclear Fuel*, reported in February 1983 that reprocessed fuel from the Rajasthan reactor could yield annually enough weapon rate plutonium for ten Hiroshima-sized bombs. It can reasonably be inferred that a similar capability exists in other countries which, under encouragement from the nuclear industry, have installed nuclear reactors.

An important international principle is at stake here, because the cornerstone of the International Atomic Energy Agency's regulatory scheme is that civilian nuclear materials and facilities should never be used for military purposes.

With nearly a dozen nations already in possession of nuclear weapons stockpiles, or the necessary technology to make them, and with an abandonment by the superpowers of even the pretence of seeking nuclear disarmament, the prospect of avoiding a nuclear war within the next decade seems remote, unless altered attitudes emerge. A limited conflict is a totally unrealistic concept, for if nuclear warheads start exploding on the territories of the superpowers, an all out nuclear exchange will be difficult to prevent.

These possibilities have now been rendered more frightening by the neutron bomb, which if exploded 200 metres above the ground will immediately kill or cause a two-day death agony to anyone within a distance of 700 metres. Buildings will be preserved intact: a macabre environmental setting for the post-nuclear war era.

Actual nuclear attack is provided for by such documents as the UN Security Council Resolutions on Security Assurances (adopted by the Security Council at its meeting on 19 June 1968), which affirms an intention to give immediate assistance to any non nuclear-weapon state which is a party to the Treaty on Non-Proliferation of Nuclear Weapons and which is a victim of an act or an object of a threat of nuclear aggression. So also, the US, by its declaration made in the Security Council (at its meeting on 17 July 1968) has affirmed its intention to seek immediate Security Council action to provide assistance to such a non-nuclear weapon state.

Such provisions are safeguards, but they also intensify dangers through the interplay of power politics; in other words, a nuclear conflagration in any part of the world will draw the great powers into conflict.

In the interest of world peace, clear agreement needs to be reached internationally on the legal status of nuclear weapons.

In 1961, the General Assembly declared that the use of

nuclear weapons would violate the letter and spirit of the UN Charter and constitute a crime against mankind. This resolution was opposed by the US government, which continued to oppose all formal and international efforts to withdraw legitimacy from nuclear weapons.

Although in the Korean war and the Vietnam war the US refrained from using or threatening to use nuclear weaponry, the official US position insists on the right to initiate a nuclear response to enemy aggression.

Many justifications have been advanced in support of US opposition to declaring nuclear weapons illegal. Among them are the need for European security, America's overall world role, the need for a context of general and complete disarmament if nuclear weapons are to be eliminated, the danger of restricting choice in future international situations, and the US's use of nuclear weapons against Hiroshima and Nagasaki in 1945. In the view of some writers, the US has consequently developed a defensive attitude towards the use of nuclear weapons.[35]

If international law has been slow to condemn the use of nuclear weapons, there has been in some national legal systems, for example, in Japan, a clear condemnation of their use. The constitution of the Republic of Palau, in a provision worthy of emulation by more powerful and developed countries, bans nuclear, chemical and biological warfare materials from the islands and their territorial waters.

Space War

Neither the US nor the USSR is anxious to halt the race for technological superiority in military space warfare, owing to the seductive nature of the technology which will destroy enemy satellites; it is to satellite information that attack and defence mechanisms on both sides are geared. The US alone operates forty military satellites.

Anti-satellite weapons based in space themselves become fresh military targets, for if either nation's early warning systems are destroyed, its defence capabilities are crippled. It is a mistake to suppose that a war in space will save lives on earth. Space adds to the danger of possible worldwide conflict.

The weaponry planned for space includes interception satellites, of which the Soviets are known to have launched seventeen between October 1978 and April 1980. The US has recently developed the miniature homing intercept vehicle that would beam in on the target satellite's infra-red radiation and destroy it by a high-speed collision. In addition, satellite-destroying lasers are planned, and the space shuttle has been used for testing tracking and targeting devices. A prime target will be Soviet satellites, the ocean surveillance of which guides Soviet submarines at sea.

Attempts to limit the technology can always be defeated, because the same technology can be developed in a different guise. The infra-red homing mechanism, for example, is also part of the anti-ballistic missile programme and can be used in space attacks.

When laser weapons are placed in space, a new dimension will be added to the insecurity of our environment. There is no doubt that the US and the USSR will move inexorably towards this position unless anti-satellite weapons are limited by treaty.

Chemical Warfare
Since 1975 there has been a resurgence of activity in chemical warfare preparations in the US and presumably also in the USSR. US chemical war research expenditure has mounted from $29 million in 1976 to $106 million in 1981.[36] On 24 July 1979, a pressure group called the American Citizens for Honesty in Government claimed that it had obtained an army technical report under the *Freedom of Information Act* which showed that the US had stockpiled 50 tonnes of a powerful hallucinogenic drug. The drug was so potent that this quantity could reduce ten times the earth's population – 40 thousand million people – to a state of complete helplessness for several days.[37]

Appalling effects of chemical warfare were seen during World War I, when hydrogen cyanide and mustard gas were among the weapons which caused 1,300,000 casualties, including 90,000 deaths and 100,000 permanent disabilities. The signatories of the 1925 Geneva Protocol pledged not to be the first users of chemical weapons in future wars, but their use in retaliation is therefore not ruled out. Unlike biological weapons (germ warfare), the use of which was completely renounced by the US in 1969, chemical weapons remain a very live part of its arsenal: the US is estimated to have 37,000 tonnes of mustard gas and about 130,000 tonnes of nerve gas which, with other chemicals, total about 400,000 tonnes. These are stored at nine depots in the US and West Germany.[38] Three million projectiles for various grades of artillery are among this stock. The corresponding Soviet figures are not known.

An added danger, not present in the nuclear field, is that the preparation of chemical weaponry is difficult to detect or monitor. The production of vast quantities of similar chemicals in industry is continuously in progress.

In the US, a new arsenal of chemical weaponry – the binary nerve gas weapons – are being built. They consist of two chemicals which are harmless when in isolation but lethal when mixed in a spinning shell.

Chemical weaponry is another environmental peril of the late twentieth century. A chemical weapons treaty must be developed.

Legal and Human Rights

The rights which thus stand vitiated, whether they are rights to aesthetic and recreational enjoyment, rights to life and health, or rights to participation in the earth's resources need for their protection the recognition of some basic new approaches and principles.

The Principle of Trusteeship

The trust concept in law means that a person who may be in charge of property, and may be its legal owner, may be responsible for preserving it for someone else. Thus the trustee of property would be prevented from selling or damaging it because that would defeat the rights of the person for whose benefit it is held. We need some similar principle to conserve the rights of future generations to the resources of the earth, for human rights involve not only the rights of those alive but also of those yet to be born, but they are rights

which legal systems in the western tradition have traditionally ignored. The human rights dialogue of the future must
derive some wisdom from the many ancient systems – Chinese, African, Melanesian, to name a few – which do not
entitle the present generation to deal with the environment
on the footing of absolute ownership. The trustee principle
is important in this field and must form the basis of future
environmental law.

The Principle of Limited Ownership

Although people may have property and the right to enjoy
it, or the right to trade freely and build up their industrial
enterprises, these rights should not encroach on the rights
of every member of the community to clean air, pure water,
and a healthy environment. The right to do as one pleases
with one's property will become progressively circumscribed
in the public interest. Keeping fertile land fallow, destroying
foodstuffs, or slaughtering livestock to sustain price levels
are some illustrations of the exercise of absolute ownership
which will be out of tune with the property principles of the
future.

The Principle of Community Ownership

Property, such as seashores, sanctuaries, game reserves, and
rivers, cannot be privately owned; it belongs to everyone.
Likewise, the high seas and the air space above them belong
to all nations and not to any particular one.

Under the principle of common ownership, commercial
use or exploitation of any of these resources must be paid
for. Within nations, the payment should be to national governments. Where the property belongs to the world community, payment should be to a world resources fund. It is
unfair that those who turn world resources into an arena for
private profit making should not have to make a payment
to the world community, especially in a world where genuine
sources of international revenue are lacking. There is no
reason in principle why countries using the high seas or the
air space over them should not pay an international tax.
Mining rights on the ocean floor as well as satellite use of
the stratosphere should similarly be taxable.

A World Environmental Fund

Much of the pollution of the planet's air and water is a result of the activities of the technologically advanced countries. It has been estimated, for example, that the average US citizen puts as much pressure on the environment as a hundred Indian citizens.[39] This raises the question to what extent industrialized nations should compensate the others for environmental damage. A world environmental fund is needed to redress the balance.

In 1972, the United Nations Conference on the Human Environment produced an action plan which included a proposal for an environment fund based on involuntary subscriptions. There was some support from the developed countries for a contribution by developed countries in addition to the 7 per cent target for economic aid, and compensation by a transfer of funds from rich countries to developing countries. The reason for this is that the developed countries developed their industries at a time when there was no requirement to observe environmental standards. Developing countries cannot afford the expense of meeting environmental standards and need to be helped if they are to observe them. Moreover, the developed countries have already polluted the seas and the atmosphere which are the common heritage of all mankind. International law is beginning to accept the principle that the one who pollutes must pay.

Principles of Pollution Control

Most pollution is caused by private profit-making activities. While the profits made find their way into private pockets, the damage to the environment is repaired if at all from public funds. In effect, society subsidizes these industries, and the community pays for the enrichment of a few. The cost of environmental repair should justly be charged on the profits earned at the expense of the environment.

The cost of developing adequate pollution standards is immense and is usually borne by the consumer in the additional cost of products; alternatively, the additional costs price products out of the market. The preservation of the environment involves a search for a balance between these two positions. Some other approaches include granting subsidies to polluters to reduce their pollution; regulating polluters by laws which are strictly enforced; viewing pollution as a privilege for which a licence must be obtained; developing a polluter pays principle, by which the polluter bears the cost of rectification of damage; and taxing polluters at a fixed rate per unit for the pollution that they cause.

Compensation

Compensation for people who have suffered from pollution has been given a lot of attention in Japan in the context of Minamata disease. A research team from Kumamoto University showed that the disease was caused by poisoning as a result of people eating fish and shellfish caught in Minamata Bay. Further research showed that the fish and shellfish had been contaminated with methyl mercury compounds discharged from the Minamata company of the Chisso Corporation. In March 1973, damages were awarded against the Chisso Corporation, but afterwards hundreds of people were diagnosed as afflicted by the disease. The pollution-related health damage compensation law was passed in 1974 providing for seven types of compensation benefits: medical care benefits and expenses, disability compensation, survivors' compensation, lump-sum survivors' compensation, child compensation allowances, medical care allowances, and funeral expenses.

The law divided Japan into zones, and sufferers in zones where pollutants led to an increased incidence of disease were certified to receive compensation for medical expenses and lost wages. A novel and important feature of this system was that compensation was based not on legal evidence of causality but on scientific evidence of probability. Traditional legal proof requires a linking of cause and effect, which is difficult in an individual case. Mere probability would be insufficient to establish liability for legal damages, as where a chemical industry worker claims to have a cancerous condition as a result of his or her work. This new procedure could provide a useful alternative remedy.

Giving Rights to the Environment

Traditionally, an inanimate object or an animal cannot have

rights. Litigation on an environmental issue, therefore, can never be brought in the name of the valley, lake or species threatened. Yet the law by a fiction has given legal status to such non-persons as corporations and ships. Environmentalists argue that traditional restraints should be broken to give legal status to the environment. Justice William O. Douglas of the US Supreme Court, well known for his love of America's wide open spaces, has argued that an entity such as an endangered river should be recognized as a possible party to an action and that it could speak through those who have a meaningful relation to it, such as fishermen, canoeists, or zoologists.[40] Other jurists argue that the time has come to give legal standing to natural objects[41] and for legal systems to speak of the environment as having legal rights. Some customary legal systems, such as the African, accord a very special status to land. Western jurisprudence may need to throw aside its conservatism in this area.

Environmental campaigners face severe disadvantages where they are up against powerful corporations. Ralph Nader has recorded the inability of the citizen under current legal provisions to elicit basic information from large organizations, which use to great advantage all the secrecy which corporate anonymity permits them.

Laws compelling public disclosure of matters of concern to environmentalists are specially required in Australia, where laws compelling governments and other authorities to disclose information are weak.

Inequality is further increased when resources are compared. Activists sustain their campaigns on enthusiasm and public spiritedness. Polluters have vast machines at their disposal and are sustained by profit. Powerful lobby groups work for them and even at legislative level they are able, because of their legal resources, to resist pressure from the environmentalists.

Legal procedures need to be devised to strengthen the hand of environmentalists. Old common law principles denying them status to sue unless they have property need to be abrogated. Screens of corporate ownership and responsibility must be penetrated and duties of disclosure made more rigorous. Legal support should be made available at public expense. A permanent public interest lobby must be maintained. In the expressive words of Justice Brandeis, one of the best known among former judges of the US Supreme Court, 'sunlight is the best disinfectant'.

Positive Environmental Action

A proper regard to a clean environment as a human right calls for affirmative action to create a rich environment. There must be plans not only for protection of nature but also for restoring and fostering nature where it has been damaged. Here there is also scope for legislation for nature conversation and restoration, an area in which legal activity is as yet in its infancy.

Developing Environmental Law

Most environmental law is made by the legislature. There is also scope for its development by judges in the traditional manner of English law. Much pioneering work in this area was done by Professor Joseph Sax of Michigan, who drafted an open-ended Michigan statute so that the courts would be stimulated to set standards in the context of actual problems and to give them a flexibility that would facilitate their handling of new developments in technology. The statute gave the citizen an unqualified right to institute environmental actions which he or she hoped would 'set the stage for the development of a common law of environmental quality'.

The fear expressed when the Michigan act was passed that an unqualified right to institute action could lead to a flood of frivolous claims has proved to be unfounded. A later study of litigation under the act has revealed that since its enactment six years earlier, it has been used in 119 cases – an average of twenty – in a jurisdiction in which there were 600,000 civil cases in the circuit courts in the same period.[42]

An important feature of the Michigan legislation is that it does not allow for costs to be awarded to an unsuccessful plaintiff, which must act as a deterrent against frivolous actions.

The concept of environmental protection is gaining ground and with this there is a greater judicial readiness to devise new concepts, principles, and standards. It has been said by some students of the common law that the great eras of judicial innovativeness are at an end. Perhaps environmental law is one of the significant fields left in which there will be much scope for a noteworthy judicial contribution to the fashioning of the law.

Environmental Education

Recommendation 96 of the Stockholm Conference on the Human Environment 1972 called for the development of environmental education as one of the most critical elements of an all-out attack on the world's environmental crisis.[43] The crisis can only be understood in the context of the social, economic and human rights perspectives outlined in the UN Declaration of the New International Economic Order. In 1979, the Belgrade Charter Framework for Environmental Education stated that the framework for a new environmental education must be laid within the context of the new international economic order. It also recognized that new knowledge, skills, values, and attitudes are the keys to a better quality of environment and a better quality of life.

The two preliminary objectives set out by the Belgrade charter were an embodiment of combined environmental, economic, and human rights perspectives. The first requires each nation to clarify the meaning of such basic concepts as 'quality of life' and 'human happiness' within the context of the environment. The second aims at improving people's well-being.

No solution can be achieved unless the world is made aware of and concerned about the environment. Indeed, the charter's governing philosophy is that no governmental or policy approaches can begin to improve the world environment unless the youth of the world receives a new kind of education.

Criminalizing Ecocide

Those who damage the eco-system have so far been dealt with essentially by the civil law. The sanctions of the civil law are basically through damages, which the affluent commercial operator or corporation can pay quite easily. They can therefore afford to flout the law of the environment.

In many senses, however, they are more culpable than those who commit traditional crimes, such as robbery or assault. The damage they cause is universal and extends to succeeding generations. They do so deliberately and for private gain. The time is ripe to bring such activity within the ambit of the criminal law, making environmental or ecological crime a standard section of each country's penal code, carrying sanctions of heavy fines and imprisonment. Ecocide may indeed take its place with genocide as one of the cardinal crimes against humanity.

The international lawyer, Professor Richard Falk, put forward in 1973 proposals for the adoption of an International Convention on the Crime of Ecocide as a result of the military defoliation of the Vietnamese countryside. Such a crime is committed par excellence by the detonation of a nuclear device, but it can also be committed in many other ways: by making the human habitat seriously damaging to health, by creating nuclear hazards in peacetime, by crippling life support systems, by developing various forms of military technology, by diminishing the aesthetic and recreational enjoyment of the planet, or by denying to most people a reasonable participation in the earth's resources.

Chapter 7

Humanness and Human Dignity

The confluence of Greek and Judaeo-Christian traditions provided western legal systems with their basic concepts for 2,000 years. The integrity of the human personality, the inviolability of the person, and the freedom of his or her intellect became central values around which the law built its protections. Notions that people exercise freewill, that their creation is beyond human power, that each person is unique, and that each person has his or her own personality lent strength and authority to these central themes.

Scholars such as Aquinas further elevated the human role, showing that human reason had a place alongside divine revelation in the scheme of the universe. The eighteenth-century philosophers exalted human reason by declaring it to be the framework within which all knowledge was to be assessed. Immanuel Kant taught humanity to view the individual will as sacrosanct and humans as ends in themselves. Historical events asserted and reasserted the equality of man. These various strands – people the central figures in creation, people the unique creatures knowing no duplicates, people the repositories of an inviolable will, people the holders of sacrosanct personalities, people the arbiter of their destinies through freewill, people who know no other person as their creators, people so infinite in value that all other people can only be equals, people in whom no other person can have property, and people as ends in themselves – were the strands of humanness, as law and western civilization saw them. On this foundation were built the various legal protections of the body, personality, reputation, privacy, family rights, the sanctity of contract as representing the consensus of free-willing minds, and the notion of civil and criminal responsibility.

Science is undermining these concepts. As we have seen,

mind manipulation techniques are undermining freewill, concentrations of capital and technology are negating equality, technological intrusions on privacy are denigrating personality, long-distance scanners and transmitters are undermining concepts of trespass, and genetic engineering is altering concepts of people as ends in themselves, as having no creators and no owners.

As these concepts are undermined, the traditional legal views of responsibility, rights, duties, guilt, innocence, ownership, possession, parental power and responsibility, will also change.

We are moving into the unprecedented era when the laboratory growth of foetuses and human/animal chimeras may force us to reconsider the meaning of humanness, preselection of sex may alter concepts of sexual equality, elimination of the need for paternity may destroy family law, organ transplants may produce spare parts banks, research dangerous to humanity may restrain the quest for knowledge, shortages of earth's resources may spawn totalitarian governments, and computers may regiment our way of living.

Law can look on with apathy only at the price of abdicating its historic role as protector of the human personality.

The Quality of Humanness

When we speak of human rights we tend to assume that there is a clearly recognizable entity known as a human being to which 'human rights' attach. This assumption needs to be examined in the context of scientific advances which work at the fringes of the beginning and end of human life and tinker with the human body and mind.

Science can keep turning up new factual data, such as the manner in which the brain cells or the nervous system function, but the value-laden question, what is the subject of human rights, is more than science can answer.

Some of the principal philosophical guidelines suggested at various times have depended on attributes of bodily form or mental capacity or on the possession of a soul or some spiritual quality. Unfortunately, all of these, both individually and collectively, are found wanting.

Bodily Characteristics

The human form is not always recognizable in every member of the species. Monstrosities sadly appear from time to time, defying every definition of form. Supervening diseases, such as the 'elephant man' disease, can alter grotesquely the human form. Although some legal systems deny monstrosities the status of human beings, modern humanitarian sentiment is of a contrary view. Human form by itself is an unsatisfactory index of humanness.

Mental Capacity

The absence of a brain, congenital idiocy, and varying degrees of mental incapacity do not deprive a new-born child of a legal status. Supervening circumstances, such as an illness or accident which reduce a person to the level of a totally mindless and vegetable existence, cannot deprive him of the quality of humanness. The mindlessness of a deep and continuing coma or of a sleeping sickness which persists for years falls within the same category.

The Soul

The law, in its early stages, held that 'ensoulment', the time when the soul enters the body, generally fixed around forty days after conception, was a prerequisite of legal rights. Such a spiritual attribute, in whatever form, has long been thought a distinguishing feature of the human race. Across religious and cultural differences, however, it is not possible to postulate this quality as a universal test of humanness.

Many other tests have been suggested from time to time as marking off the human from other species. Among these are the ability to act autonomously, independent of the dictates of instinct; the ability to make and use tools; the ability to argue and reason; the ability to anticipate and plan; the ability to communicate through speech; the ability to use symbols; a quality of self-consciousness; a sense of responsibility; and an ability to imagine and conceptualize.

Clearly, the absence of one or more of these characteristics will not deprive a person of the quality of humanness.

Uniqueness has sometimes been suggested as a distinguishing feature, on the basis that every human being could never have a duplicate. Such a unique individual thus has unique value and is deserving of every protection. The test of uniqueness does not stand examination, however, for uniqueness plainly exists among all mammalian creatures (except perhaps in relation to the cloned creatures of the future).

It is my view that if we are to take a stand it should be on the lines that a person biologically of the species *homo sapiens* is a subject of human rights whatever the mutations of his bodily form or the weaknesses of his intellect.[1]

The Beginning of Humanness

Legal attempts to define the beginning of humanness have been unsuccessful. One of the latest attempts is in a bill, known as the 'human life' bill, debated in the US Senate in 1982. Introduced by Republican Jesse Helms of North Carolina, it is framed on the basis that 'present-day scientific evidence indicates a significant likelihood that actual human life exists from conception'. If successful, the bill will protect life from conception and outlaw abortion and intra-uterine devices which obstruct the implantation of the fertilized egg.

Although there is no question about the beginning of *life* with the fertilization of the egg, the question when *human* life begins is loaded with difficulties. Let us consider some possible tests.

Fertilization (zero time)

Immediately on conception the unique genetic quality of the foetus is set. Only a small proportion of fertilized eggs are implanted in the uterus; however, about two-thirds never reach their destination and die off without their existence being ever known, although without a doubt they are living human cells, with all the potential to develop into full human beings.

Implantation (six days)

This usually occurs about six days after fertilization. During these six days, the process of cell division has gone on. Still infinitesimal, the little speck immediately produces considerable changes in the mother's body.

Heart function (four weeks)
The faint beats of the infant heart are detectable around the fourth week. If heart beat is an important index of life, then life has begun at this stage. The classical elements of the adult electro-cardiogram can be obtained at five weeks.

The acquisition of human form (six weeks)
By the sixth week the foetus begins to assume a form which can be recognized as human. The primitive skeletal system is by now fully developed. No more than 1.5 centimetres in length, it also acquires the facility of independent movement.

Brain function (twelve weeks)
We do not know exactly when the brain begins to set off waves. At twelve weeks, they are certainly detectable. If brain function is the criterion of human life, then human life has begun. Moreover, the child has become very active, kicking its legs and turning its feet. It can also squint and frown – the latter a clear indication of sensation.[2]

First trimester
Nearly the same as the above, this is the test laid down by the US Supreme Court in its *Roe* v. *Wade* decision.

Nervous system (twenty-four weeks)
This is fully functioning at twenty-four weeks, although some authorities would place it much earlier.

Birth (nine months)
This has been the *sine qua non* in many legal systems for according rights to the new member of the human community, however premature the birth.

These tests represent the scientific view. Theological and legal views must also be considered.

Canon Law
The early fathers of the church drew no distinction between stages of foetal development, prohibiting abortion absolutely. This view was later modified under the influence of St Jerome, [3] and St Augustine, the fifth-century theologian who laid the foundations of much Catholic dogma, argued that 'there cannot be a live soul in a body that lacks sensation when it is not formed with flesh and so not yet endowed with

sense'.[4] Augustine was influenced by Aristotelian biology in reaching this conclusion, for Aristotle had predicated a period of forty days for the male and eighty days for the female before the foetus was 'ensouled'. St Thomas Aquinas, the twelfth-century Catholic theologian, thought that sensation and movement were the only practical tests of formation or 'ensoulment'.[5]

For many centuries the Aristotelian distinction between the souled and the unsouled foetus continued to influence the canon law, and the distinction drawn between the formed and the unformed foetus resulted in the view that abortion of the latter was less than homicide. In 1621, Paola Zacchia, who wrote on medico-legal questions from the standpoint of the Catholic Church, attacked the Aristotelian doctrine of ensoulment as an 'imaginary thing'.[6] This attack gradually influenced a change of theological opinion until, in the nineteenth century, Pope Pius IX removed the distinction[7] under a Bull which made every direct taking of human life after fertilization liable to the penalty of excommunication.[8] Later papal pronouncements have confirmed this position: in 1951, Pope Pius XII condemned abortion as a 'grave and illicit attempt on inviolable human life', no matter at what moment it occurred in the development of the foetus;[9] in 1965, Vatican Council II specified: 'From the moment of its conception life must be guarded with the greatest care, and abortion and infanticide are unspeakable crimes.'[10] Modern genetic knowledge that each person receives his or her unique genetic code at the moment of conception is invoked in support of this view.[11]

Jewish Law
Jewish law never endowed the foetus with the status of a born human being.[12] Thus a woman sentenced for a capital crime would be executed irrespective of her condition provided the birth process had not already started. The death penalty for the killing of a born child was inflicted only if the child was a result of a full-term pregnancy, and in the case of a premature birth, capital punishment would not be incurred unless the child was at least thirty days old.[13] An interesting facet of the Jewish position was that the child did

not have full rights as a human until the forehead was presented in the process of birth.

Common Law

The distinction between the formed and the unformed foetus entered English law as part of a shared European tradition. As English law developed its own principles, however, it began to pinpoint birth as the criterion for the definition of life, holding the killing of a child born alive to be murder but of a quickened foetus to be 'a great misprision but no murder'.[14]

Nevertheless, the notion of quickening (the stage at which the woman feels the child move within her) survived in the English law, for it was only the killing of the quickened foetus that was misprision. This distinction was abolished in 1837,[15] but the notion of quickening still retained relevance in the English law until 1931 in the form of a rule under which a woman condemned of a capital crime could receive a respite if she was 'quick with child'.[16] Abortion was a felony at common law and remained so until 1968.

Jewish and English law concur that the killing of an unborn child is not homicide, the foetus not being viewed as a living person. Under canon law, however, foetal life is as inviolable as that of a living person, and even therapeutic abortion (that is, abortion, for example, where the mother's life is in danger) is contrary to canon law principles. Therapeutic abortion becomes permissible under canon law if the lives of the mother and child are both threatened as, for example, a result of ectopic pregnancies and cancer of the cervix.

These restrictions on therapeutic abortion were not shared by the Jewish or the English systems under which the foetal life did not share in full degree the 'humanness' of the mother. It was possible, therefore, to end the foetal life for the sake of preserving the mother's life,[17] a notion which the English law extended in 1938 to cover both mental and physical risk to the mother.

In the case which produced this extension of the law,[18] a doctor was prosecuted for aborting a fifteen-year-old girl who was raped by four soldiers and ran a serious risk of mental illness if she gave birth to a child. On behalf of the doctor, it was argued that 'preserving the life of the mother' – the test set by the *Infant Life (Preservation) Act*, 1919 – covered both physical and mental risk to the mother. The doctor was acquitted, the court formulating the test in terms that if the doctor is satisfied that the probable result of the continuance of the pregnancy is to make the woman a physical or mental wreck, the jury were entitled to hold that he was operating for the purpose of preserving the life of the woman.

Under the *Abortion Act* of 1967, in assessing the risk to the mother, account could be taken not only of the woman's actual circumstances but also of her foreseeable ones; the law also added two new grounds: risk of injury to the physical or mental health of any existing children of the woman's family and substantial risk of her giving birth to a severely deformed child.[19]

In covering risks to the existing children of a pregnant woman and taking account of the woman's actual and foreseeable environment, the English law goes further than the Australian.

The Australian legislation turns on the interpretation of the word *unlawfully* in statutes such as the *Victorian Crimes Act* (s.10(1)) which makes it an offence wilfully and *unlawfully* to cause the death of a child capable of being born alive. (A woman who has been pregnant for a period of twenty-eight weeks or more is presumed pregnant of a child capable of being born alive.)

In 1969 the Victorian Supreme Court in Davidson's case[20] ruled that for an abortion to be lawful the accused must have honestly believed on reasonable grounds that the act done by him or her was necessary to preserve the woman from a serious danger to her life or physical or mental health and that the act of abortion was not out of proportion to the danger to be averted. The New South Wales Supreme Court in Wald's case[21] followed Davidson's case and held it was for the jury to decide whether there was any economic, social, or medical ground or reason which in their view would constitute reasonable grounds for an honest belief on the part of the accused that there would be serious danger to mental or physical health. This ruling was wider than the Victorian one, in permitting economic, social, and medical grounds to be taken into account in determining the danger to the woman's physical or mental health.

South Australia has dealt with unlawful abortions by an act dealing with cases in which one doctor may act on his own opinion in emergency situations but in general requires that two doctors examine the patient and form an opinion.[22] The provision is restricted to women who have resided in South Australia for at least two months before the abortion. The law otherwise differs little from the Victorian one. In Western Australia, Queensland and Tasmania, the position is more restrictive.

When reference is made to the rights of the foetus or to its 'humanness', it is against this tradition that the argument needs to be appraised. It remains only to mention some landmarks in the US system which have considerably influenced current attitudes to the foetus.

In *Roe* v. *Wade* the US Supreme Court held that the foetus was not a person under the constitution. In his judgment, Justice Blakmun pointed out that when the disciplines of medicine, philosophy and theology are unable to arrive at any consensus on foetal rights, the Supreme Court could not make a decision and override the rights of the pregnant woman.[23]

This view is not widely shared in other countries and has aroused much criticism within the US. The International Code of Medical Ethics, for example, compiled in 1949 following a meeting of the World Medical Association in Geneva, and confirmed at its meeting in 1950 at Oslo, states that 'a doctor must always bear in mind the importance of preserving human life from the time of conception until death.[24] In 1975, the Supreme Court of West Germany affirmed under its constitution the right of human life to be protected at all stages of development. There was even in the dissenting judgment an acceptance of the existence of human life *in utero*.[25]

French law is silent on the definition of the beginning of life but administrative rules require the registration of embryos more than 180 days old and recommend the declaration of embryos after the sixth week of gestation.[26]

In the US, in 1975, at the request of Congress, the National Commission for the Protection of Human Subjects of Biomedical and Behavioural Research released its final report, called 'Research on the Foetus'. The commission heard a broad range of views from theologians, philosophers, physicians, scientists, lawyers, public officials, and private citizens. Among its recommendations are that therapeutic research may be conducted on the foetus, non-therapeutic research may, with certain safeguards, be carried out on a foetus to be aborted, and that dead foetal material may be used for research purposes that were consistent with commonly held convictions about respect for the dead.

The commission's report has been widely criticized. Professor David W. Louisell, a dissenting commissioner, criticized the recommendations as sacrificing the interests of innocent human life to social need. Another commentator pointed out that the fact that the unborn is not a 'person' in the federal constitution does not make it true that the unborn is not a legal person for other purposes.[27]

If a strong case can be made out for according humanness to the unborn foetus, there is no reason in principle why this quality of humanness should not apply to a developing foetus in laboratory conditions or in the test tube.

What is important in the discussion is not the site where the development takes place but the entity which is under development. If it is human, if it is unique, if it is an individual, if at some unspecified time it can feel sensation and pain, if it is clearly a genetically distinguishable entity which is maturing into a human, it must be protected by the law. The health of the mother, the social good of the community, and the interests of the unborn child must exist as counterweights of sufficient gravity if they are to displace the unborn individual's need, as a human-to-be, to be exempted from hurt or harm.

The law with one hand grants increasing rights in tort to the unborn and with the other takes away the basic right to live, sanctioning arbitrary killing on the one hand and saying on the other that the dead tissue thus created can be used for foetal experimentation 'with due regard for customs relating to respect for the dead'.

The basic argument against foetal rights is the uncertainty

of scientific knowledge about the ability of the foetus to feel. If there is uncertainty, it seems apposite to apply the usual rule which the law applies in crime: if there is doubt, give to the person who will suffer, the benefit of the doubt. With the unborn, the creature which has been shown to respond to stimuli, we are prepared by law to sanction the infliction of pain, dismemberment and death, resolving the uncertainty against the sufferer. Some day, if more light is thrown on this problem and it is shown graphically that the foetus feels pain and suffers, we will not be in a position to undo the legal and moral injustices we now condone.

This is not to hold up a blanket argument against abortion. Competing needs must always be matched, and that is one of the prime tasks of the law.

If the foetus is entitled to all the rights of a human on the day of its birth, it is difficult to see why, in the state of modern scientific knowledge, it should be denied human rights the day before, when it is as fully formed and when, by a surgeon's decision to perform a caesarean section, it could even then see the light of day. The law is adept at distinguishing cases and attempting to justify differences of treatment of similar cases on the basis that the differences between them are serious enough to attract differences of consequence. On the most serious of all decisions the law can face – the decision to accord or withhold recognition of humanity – it rests its case on a distinction, without a difference. The supreme principle of distributive justice, that like cases must be treated alike, which lies at the root of western legal systems, is violated.

Another cluster of human rights issues centres around new developments in surgery performed on a malformed foetus while the foetus is still in the womb. Research is fast advancing in this area, and a world centre to consider the resulting issues has opened in Winnipeg. The ethical issues are receiving consideration in Australia from such bodies as the Ethics Committee of the Queen Victoria Hospital in Melbourne.

The Infinite Value of Human Life
Traditional Judaeo-Christian thinking accorded an infinite value to the human personality, based on the *imago dei* prin-

ciple: that humans are cast in the image of God. No other value can therefore be measured against humanity.

Viewed in the context of medical technology, this means that a doctor cannot put any other values in the scales against the value of human life. The cost of treatment or the quality of life for the patient would be wholly extraneous. Theoretically, therefore, a human life should be kept in existence as long as medical science can do so even at a cost of a million dollars.

In a practical world, such theoretical approaches are clearly not always possible, and the most traditional of doctors would readily admit that an additional hour or two of life would not justify spending vast amounts of money to keep one patient alive.

The moment such a concession is made, we at once circumscribe the concept of the infinite worth of life. The question that follows is where do you draw the line. The issue becomes pointed when expensive technology is involved.

Much as we value human life, we are forced to weigh up the prolonging of life against the massive costs to the community. Policy decisions will need to be made on whether a kidney machine or particular drugs should be acquired for one patient, when the same sum of money would save a hundred children from malnutrition or equip the community with five extra hospital beds.

In the years ahead, however, not only the cost of treatment but also a patient's quality of life will be weighed up against life. People so handicapped that their quality of life is impaired range from a patient suffering from a minor illness to a child born without a brain. Somewhere between these extremes, the quality of life reaches a level where there would be almost universal agreement that a life so lived is not worth living.

In assessing a person's quality of life, some doctors consider the capacity to experience joy, to live a self-conscious life, to look forward to the future, to communicate, and to respond to others.

Some objections to these criteria are that there will not generally be any agreement about them; human lives cannot be divided into those worth living and those not worth living; and the decision whether life is worth living is a subjective and private one.

In May 1981, in Illinois, Siamese twins were born. Their trunks were joined and they had between them two legs and a vestigial short leg. The parents decided that they could not bear the burden of supporting the children, and the children survived, apparently because a nurse had fed them. In the resulting prosecution of the doctor and the parents for attempted murder, no hospital staff could be found who were willing to give evidence for the prosecution. The case was dismissed.

In June 1979, Christopher Derkacs, a Down's Syndrome child of twenty-three months, died in the Princess Margaret Hospital in Perth. It was alleged that the child died because necessary medical treatment was deliberately withheld when the child was suffering from a respiratory complaint. The case attracted much attention and ended with an open finding by the coroner.

The Australian case focused attention on an issue which was to be highlighted in many subsequent UK, US and European ones. What does one do when a grossly defective child, for whom life may be a continuing misery, is in need of elaborate medical attention?

Dr Leonard Arthur of the Derbyshire City Hospital faced this question when, in June 1980, he delivered John Pearson, also a Down's Syndrome baby. The parents rejected the child claiming that they did not have the financial or emotional strength to sustain it. The child died in three days, as a result, it was alleged, of instructions by the doctor that it be given nursing care only. The doctor was charged with murder and after an eighteen-day trial he was acquitted, much to the relief of the British Paediatricians' Association.

An Oxford don, the secretary of EXIT (a voluntary euthanasia society in the UK), was convicted on 30 October 1982 by a unanimous verdict at London's Central Criminal Court of helping a person suffering from terminal cancer to kill himself. The judge imposed a sentence of two and a half years imprisonment, one of the heaviest sentences for aiding suicide. 'Not only was he deliberately flouting the law', said the judge, 'but using the society, the object of which was to get the law changed, as a cover to jump the gun and make it necessary to change the law.' The accused shouted defiantly as he was led down to the cells, 'That shows the idiocy of the present law.' The court heard details during the trial of how the secretary put terminally ill people in touch with a person who helped them to kill themselves with the aid of a suicide kit of drugs, plastic bags, and alcohol. It was not alleged that the secretary had acted for motives other than compassion. On appeal, the sentence of thirty months was reduced to eighteen months, and the court observed that justice could be done to the accused and the public interest by reducing the sentence only.

In the UK, a mongoloid baby was born with an intestinal obstruction which, if untreated, would have ended her life. Surgery which could have saved her life was not performed. An emergency application was filed in court for an order directing an operation. Refused by the lower court judge, the matter was rushed in before an appeal judge who ruled in August 1981 that the operation should take place, postulating as a test, 'Is the child's life going to be so *demonstrably awful* as not to be worth living?'

A large number of similar decisions are doubtless taken daily in the hospitals of the world by doctors who use their independent and unaided discretion in determining whether a person should be permitted to live. The decision is taken in the interests of the patient, but in the absence of guidelines for the medical profession, or by law, or by the world community of doctors, the decision remains one of discretion. About 300 children suffering from spina bifida are permitted to die in the UK each year when minor intervention could save them, and many people in their eighties and nineties, whose life can be artificially prolonged, are permitted to die although medical intervention could save them.

How does one work out guidelines to meet this situation and who is to make them? Haphazard judicial decisions are not the answer. The community must contribute to such guidelines, and those working in the disciplines of theology, philosophy, sociology and psychology must contribute to the debate.

Until these aspects are sufficiently worked out and result

in legislation, the Victorian Voluntary Euthanasia Society suggests the adoption of an advance non-statutory declaration which would not legally bind the doctor but free him or her of any doubt about the wishes of the patient.

The society suggests that a copy of the declaration should be given to a solicitor or personal agent and the original deposited with the declarant's medical attendants for his or her medical file. The declaration should be witnessed by two people who have no expectation of benefiting from the declarant's death.

No discussion of euthanasia is complete without a reference to the hospice movement. In 1870, the Sisters of Charity in Dublin opened a place 'of peace and comfort for the poor of Dublin in the closing days of their lives on earth'. Descendants of that movement in Australia are the Caritas Christi Hospice in Kew, Melbourne, started in 1938 and the St Joseph's Hospice in Lismore, New South Wales, in 1937.

These were hospitals for the aged. When in more recent years medicine became more powerful in prolonging life and thereby lengthened suffering both for the patient and his or her family, a new kind of hospice came to be built on the old foundations. It aimed to help patients to live to the limit of their potential in physical strength, mental and emotional capacity and social relationships. It offered an alternative form of treatment to the acute care of the general hospital – not in opposition but as a further resource for those for whom it was no longer appropriate. St Christopher's Hospice in Kent is the prime example of this new kind of hospice. The Melbourne City Mission, with its hospice at Harold McCracken House, opened in 1979, is an Australian example of this new movement. However ill and hopeless the person, hospices believe that the shadow of approaching death can be lightened and life made more meaningful and enjoyable.

The Creation of Human Life
The power to interfere with the natural creation of human life spawns a variety of ethical and legal problems. To understand them we will need to consider the religious and moral values which underlie the law.

Theological teaching strongly emphasizes the divine origin of life and of the processes leading up to it. In the early years of artificial insemination, both Rome (Pope Pius XII, 1949) and Canterbury (1948 committee report) firmly condemned artificial insemination as a means of human procreation.

Sensing that such forms of interference with procreation might become an avenue for intrusion by the state into the area of family life, Vatican II proclaimed that decisions on the matter of generating children 'can in no way be left to the judgment of public authority'.[28] The Statement of the Catholic Bishops of the United States on Government and Birth Control (14 November 1966) likewise warned that the common good can suffer from 'public policies which tamper with the instincts of love and the sources of life'. Similar pronouncements have been made by other theologians[29] and churches.

Dissenting voices have suggested the possibility of other approaches.[30] Father de Chardin, for example, has written:

So far we have certainly allowed our race to develop at random and we have given too little thought to the question of what medical and moral factors must replace the crude forces of natural selection should we suppress them. In the course of the coming centuries it is indispensable that a nobly human form of eugenics, on a standard worthy of our personalities, should be discovered and developed.[31]

Joseph Fletcher, a Protestant theologian,[32] likens church interference with embryo research to the persecution of Galileo and criticizes the belief that the creation of life is God's function alone.

Public opinion is changing, however, which may bring with it the possibility of a shift in the rigid theological stance. A growing percentage of the population of the US and Western Europe has been conceived by artificial insemination by donor. In the US, several hundred thousand people have been conceived in this way, in the UK several hundred artificial insemination pregnancies are achieved each year, and in Australia about 1,000 such births have already occurred.[33] Against this background, legal systems will follow in the wake of popular demand and grant their full approval to the procedure. Earlier attitudes which equated artificial insemination with adultery are now outmoded, and court decisions which solemnly pronounced such a principle are not likely to be followed. Some modification of the theological position seems inevitable.

Artificial insemination by donor, however, is only in its infancy. Whereas it is now resorted to only by couples unable to conceive in the normal way, in the future it is likely to become a routine method of conception even among couples able to procreate normally, because couples could plan their children and their lives with far greater assurance than with natural mating without diminishing the quality of their sex life.

Artificial insemination by donor foreshadows some of the issues raised in in vitro fertilization.

When the first IVF baby was born to the Brown family in England, the Catholic Church, relying on the earlier pronouncement of Pope Pius XII, found the procedure contrary to the law of nature. It said that the end, namely Mr and Mrs Brown's desire for a child, was commendable but condemned the means. Rabbi Siegel, Professor of Ethics at Manhattan's Jewish Theological Seminary, argued on the other hand that the Browns were trying to obey the commandment to have children. When nature did not permit conception, it was desirable to attempt to assist nature.[34]

Arguments against IVF included that it was an example of a person attempting to play God; the home was being converted into a laboratory; the rights of the child-to-be, who was undergoing a grave risk of deformity, were not considered, and informed consent could not be given.

Julius Stone, one of the pre-eminent jurists of our time, put this case:

I admit, for example, that the techniques of in vitro human birth might lift great sorrows and burdens from some potential parents, afford comfort and solace to others. I admit also that genetic surgery and engineering may be able to mitigate gene-borne disease and disability. I would not admit that relief afforded for such cases (admirable in itself though it might be) could even begin to tip the scales against the formidable dangers to a liberty-based society to which test-tube birth or any analogue of this would open the way.[35]

He argues that there is a baseline of freedom which is increasingly under threat from developments in microbiology, genetics, neurophysiology, electronics, and pharmacology. I agree with the latter part of Stone's observation, differing only in believing that the methods of conception a couple choose are within their province to determine (subject to the public interest). The moment the procedures are resorted to outside the framework of a couple desiring a child, as, for example, when it leads to the multiple cultivation of foetuses, the law needs to step in to guard both freedom and human integrity. Even within the context of a couple desiring a child, public interest considerations involved (for example, the anonymity of the sperm donor; no special premium on particular kinds of sperm; no attempt at genetic structuring when such structuring becomes possible) need to be carefully defined and tightly enforced.

The Manipulation of the Human Mind

If the humanist sets out with an absolute proposition that interference with the mind is not permitted in any circumstances, he or she meets the argument that this has always occurred and that the early training of children seeks to inculcate in them the values and thought patterns of the community – a matter in which the child has no choice. There is no such entity, therefore, as a mind that has always been its own master. The behavioural regulators argue that it is better that regulation be done by those with an expertise in the field rather than by haphazard processes.[36]

One basis for such reasoning is that many centuries of human development have left human beings as they were when civilization started, and that many millennia of human evolution have not succeeded in transmitting altruism genetically. Hence, since technology has raced ahead while human conduct remains largely the same, it is our duty, if we have the technology, to use it for structuring a better human body and a better human mind. Another argument is that if, in the past, we interfered with the processes of nature in regard to our bodily process – witness our dependence on cooked food, or clothes – might we not do so in the future with the sharpened tools now available for producing a better mind.

Apart from these general theoretical observations, there is little room for debate that surgical techniques can, with caution, be put into service for such humane purposes as curing acute depression and curbing violent behaviour. But further legal and philosophical work needs to be done on defining the justifiable boundaries of such interference.

The concept of autonomous people, whatever their limitations, cannot be abandoned. If people can be given thought and personality by means other than influence and persuasion, and if the brain can be tampered with (otherwise than for 'treatment'), we allow a process of dehumanization. People become things; their mind becomes a manipulators' toy; their personalities reflections of other presences rather than lamps lit from within. An independent, free-willing person – the theoretical basis and fundamental value of legal systems and human rights – is cut away.

As brain science encroaches on the concept of autonomy, we need to face the problem of the control of control. If other people mould a person's thoughts and reactions, how can such controllers be guided?

A procedure as fundamental as physical interference with the brain requires the community's accumulated wisdom. A conference of physicians deciding on a course of treatment for a patient with a bodily ailment does not generally need community participation. Where the brain is involved, however, no community can afford to leave the scientists to arbitrate.

Privacy
That each person should enjoy freedom from intrusion is central to the concept of the human personality. This notion has both physical and mental dimensions. In a physical sense, every person is entitled to space beyond the immediate physical space taken up by his or her body. So with the mind. There is a realm of thought and emotion which is private and which the law is bound to protect. Modern technology is intruding on our mental and physical privacy.

Privacy laws were framed on the assumption that territorial entry or physical interference is basic to an invasion
of privacy, but these outdated laws need to be revamped.
Although it was not until the 1970s that privacy became a
serious issue for the legal profession, in 1928 Justice Brandeis
of the US Supreme Court said:

The advances in science – discovery and invention – have made it
possible for the government to effect disclosure in court of 'what
is whispered in the closet' by means far more effective than stretch-
ing the defendant upon the rack. By means of television, radium
and photography, there may some day be developed ways by which
the government could, without removing papers from secret
drawers, reproduce them in court and lay before the jury the most
intimate occurrences of the home. It is conceivable, also, that
advances in the psychic and related sciences may afford means of
exploring a man's unexpressed beliefs, thoughts and emotions.[37]

The weakness of common law is that no 'right to privacy'
has been developed.[38]

Traditional common law attitudes leave the law ill
equipped to deal with the secrecy of personal data record systems and leave citizens unable to ascertain what records are
kept on them. They give no guidance on the principles of
responsibility for incorrect recording or unauthorized or
careless disclosure of information, nor is there any general
national policy on information storage and retrieval which
can act as a guide to courts and data banks. The law is inadequate to deal with the growth of satellite communication
and international data banks.

To combat such dangers, it helps to have privacy expressly
declared to be a right of every citizen, as in France, where
an amendment to the Civil Code in 1970 declared that
'Everyone has the right to respect for his private life.' It also
helps to have legislation on invasion of privacy. The Nether-
lands Criminal Code embodied such a provision by an
amendment of 7 April 1971 making it an offence to listen
in to a conversation carried on in a dwelling or private premises by means of a technical device, other than on the instructions of the participant in the conversation, and in France,
in 1970, a law created new offences including spying by

audio-visual devices. Amendments to the Swiss Penal Code in 1969 aimed at protecting the individual's privacy against invasion by technical devices. In all legal systems, new torts and new crimes of unlawful surveillance by technological devices are needed.

The Nordic Conference of Jurists in May 1967 analysed the right to privacy as meaning the individual's right to lead his own life protected against interference with private, family and home life; interference with physical or mental integrity or moral or intellectual freedom; attacks on honour or reputation; being placed in a false light; the disclosure of irrelevant, embarrassing facts relating to private life; the use of name, identity or likeness; spying, prying, watching and besetting; interference with correspondence; misuse of private communications, written or oral; and disclosure of information given or received by a person in circumstances of professional confidence.

Technology makes nearly all of these types of interference easy.

The Standing Committee on Law and Technology of the Union Internationale des Avocats suggested an approach to privacy based upon a view of it as an essential possession to be interfered with only for the best of reasons and as sparingly as possible.

There has been much debate on whether this right is a general right, like a right of property, or whether it is a right protecting the individual against interference by the state. The Nordic Conference favoured the former view; the Legal Committee of the Consultative Assembly of the Council of Europe favoured the latter. I believe that the former view is preferable as giving more scope for development, and should therefore gain acceptance.

Privacy cannot be an absolute and unfettered right. Some surrender of privacy will be needed in the interests of society. The Nordic Conference of Jurists phrased the limitations well when it observed:

In modern society, the right to privacy, as any other human right, can never be without limitations except in the sense that nothing can justify measures which are inconsistent with the physical, mental, intellectual or moral dignity of the human person.

The Duality of Personality

Human beings are emotional and rational beings, and the legal systems they have built reflect this duality.

Scientific progress tends to allow the emotional part of our being to be submerged by the rational. All endeavour comes to be judged in the cold, dispassionate light of utility. Organization and automation take over the ordering of human affairs, and judgments requiring a combination of both elements tend to be made upon a preponderance of the one.

The emotional aspect of our nature makes a continuing contribution to the law. Concepts of morality, duty, bona fides, responsibility, and equity rely for their development on the head and heart. No dispassionate logic can pronounce on the proportions in which fact and emotion are blended in these concepts. Indeed, the reign of scientific analytical jurisprudence which held sway in western legal systems in the nineteenth century, and sought to base itself on logic alone, was a period of stunted legal growth. A blindness to social realities and to the humanitarian aspects of the law worked great social injustice, which remained until the second half of the twentieth century to be redressed.

It may be, as some have argued, that there are advantages in adapting the human being to the needs of the future. Extra strength to the arm, extra neurons to the brain, may be desirable. The research that will build into the human arm a muscular capability several times its present strength or will physically link up computer power with the human brain is already under way. The research that can lead to the production of grotesque aberrations, and indeed create human/ animal and human/plant hybrids is no longer confined to science fiction.

Before these steps are taken, we must ponder carefully whether the law is adequate to police the border between the scientifically possible and the legally prohibited. In the past, adaptations of human personality or of the human body for purposes of therapy have been permitted. Artificial limbs have been provided, artificial blood vessels and pacemakers supplied to the heart, and brain processes surgically modified. Therapy is one thing, however; deliberate change is another. We must cry halt at a stage where the human being, the basis and the ultimate value of the law, is in danger of being modified.

Chapter 8

Power, Ethics, and Responsibility

Justice Holmes, the great US jurist-judge, stressed the maxim that in law a page of history is often worth a volume of logic. The legal problems under discussion cannot be understood without seeing them in the historical context of the growth of the power of science. The tussle between science and law has passed through various phases, and the legal attitudes of one phase become outmoded as the conflict moves on to another. The contest has worked itself out on two planes: the conceptual and the practical.

The Conceptual Triumph
The conceptual ascendancy of science and technology can be viewed in various stages from the dominance of authority to the point when it capitulated and left the field to science.

In medieval Europe, the clergy saw in science a threat to their grip over the Christian mind. The doctrine that all truth was divinely revealed and contained in scripture had powerful sanctions to back it. It became a potent curb on the progress of science. The clergy used their unquestioned intellectual authority and temporal power to bring science into disrepute. The law followed hard on their heels, and the punishments provided for witchcraft were readily imposed. The mystic sanctions of religion were invoked to place scientific knowledge in the category of the black arts, and as a result the border between science and witchcraft was heavily blurred. The identification between scientific knowledge and the devil, which later found expression in the Faust legend, was a compelling part of pre-Renaissance society and belief.

The spirit of free scientific inquiry, stimulated by the resurgence of learning in the Arab world during the dark ages, began to grow in Europe when philosophers such as

Thomas Aquinas, relying partly on the work of the Arab philosophers, elevated reason and inquiry to a status of recognition alongside divine scripture.

The Renaissance brought with it a more enlightened attitude towards scientific knowledge and reduced to some extent the antagonism that had prevailed between authority and science. Francis Bacon (1561-1626), for whom there was no conflict between the truths of science and religion, followed. For Bacon knowledge could not be at war with itself, for scientific knowledge was, like theological knowledge, a subdivision of knowledge. In *New Atlantis*, Bacon elevated science and the scientist by painting a picture of a society in which there was a government by the best of the people: by technicians, architects, astronomers, geologists, biologists, physicians, chemists, economists, sociologists, psychologists and philosophers.[1] In his *Novum Organum*, he elevated scientific method into the sphere of precise experimentation.

Moreover, the spirit of inquiry at this time began to unearth new facts so concrete that no dogmas could prevail against them. The mariner's compass, the invention of gunpowder, the establishment of the printing press produced their results for all to see. The discovery of America, for example, had to be accepted, although it upset the settled ideas of the time.

The forces of tradition nevertheless did not give up the struggle without a rearguard action. The trial of Galileo for heresy was only three centuries ago, and it shocks us that a leading scientist should have been threatened with torture by a church court until he recanted his proposition that the earth moves around the sun.

Through Bacon's teaching, science could claim that the truths it discovered could lead to wealth and abundance for the community.[2] Under the influence of Bacon, science steadily advanced but significantly did not meet religion and authority in head-on confrontation.

Darwin's *Origin of Species*, published in 1859, showed that science was now staking a claim to acceptance even when its teachings directly contradicted scripture. Although a crescendo of protest rose from all sectors of the church, science was now too strong to be brought to its knees. The Darwinian confrontation represented the completion of science's emancipation from all forms of theoretical restraint. Thereafter the facts were as science laid them down, not as tradition or authority ordained. There have, of course, been notable exceptions. The Nazis banned the teachings of Jewish scientists, such as Freud and Einstein, and in 1933 burnt 25,000 books by Jewish authors. In 1925, in the US, a Tennessee teacher named John Thomas Scopes was prosecuted for violating a statute making it unlawful to teach any theory denying the method of divine creation as taught in the Bible. But these were departures from the norm. So great was the ascendancy of science that lawyers sought to adopt its methodology. The scientist's dominance was an intellectual one, however, and the practical transformation was yet to come.

The Practical Triumph

The emancipation of theoretical science did not mean that the scientist had attained a position of practical power. That was to come by slow degrees, and again from very humble beginnings.

Individual scientists have at various times been close to the centre of power by reason of their special skills, for example, Archimedes in the government of King Hiero of Syracuse, Leonardo da Vinci in the court of Ludovico Sforza, or Tycho Brahe at the court of Holy Roman Emperor Rudolph II. There were also exceptional cases of scientists, such as Benjamin Franklin or Thomas Jefferson, who were at the centre of power, but they held power in their own right and not through any fortuitous connections with science. Socially, the scientist ranked modestly, and when a bishop was paid £10,000 a year and a general £3,000 a year, Faraday's official salary at the Royal Institute was £200.[3] The scientist remained at the periphery of his nation's affairs, his scientific status affording him no passport to the centres of power or influence.

It was the world wars which proved the indispensability of scientists and brought them from the peripheries of power to its centre. Germany, for example, would have been unable to continue World War I beyond the end of 1916 without the work of its chemists. The discovery by Fritz Haber of a method of ammonia synthesis and by Wilhelm Ostwald of a method of conversion of ammonia to nitric acid supplied Germany with the nitrating agents essential for the manufacture of explosives, after supplies from Chile had been cut off in 1914.

World War II carried this trend forward because the scientist's work became indispensable to victory. Nuclear power sealed the ascendancy of scientists and gave them access to the centres of political power. Their power and influence grew in the post-war years.

Power wielded by such figures as Lord Cherwell, who was Churchill's adviser during World War II, or Sir Solly Zuckerman in later years, was a new phenomenon. Figures such as Lysenko who advised Stalin, Szilard who advised Roosevelt, Abdus Salaam who was science adviser to the president of Pakistan, and India's leading nuclear scientist, Homi Bhaba, by reason of their closeness to their heads of state, were able to brush aside bureaucrats when they wanted to pursue a scientific project.

In the post-war years, a connection developed between science and industry which made the scientist indispensable at the highest levels of commercial decision making. A similar connection existed between science and the military establishment, and science and the public service. In every sphere of activity, the scientist was at the centre of decision making. The scientific establishment thus became a new power-centre.

Few lawyers realized the nature of the problem that was growing up in their midst. If and when the day arrived when some form of scientific activity needed to be curbed in the public interest, the law was not ready conceptually or structually to meet the challenge.

Modern Swings against Science

There have been periodic swings against science in every century. Swift, for example, attacked Boyle in the seventeenth century, Blake, Goethe and Schiller attacked Newtonian philosophy in the eighteenth century, and, in the nineteenth century, a wave of romanticism represented a marked swing away from the reign of reason. These were passing phases, however, and not sustained challenges.

Today, however, a significant move against science is under way, and perhaps the concern in so many quarters about the legal questions raised in this book is one of the manifestations of this movement.

An OECD report on *Science Growth and Society*,[4] issued in 1971, analyses the changes in public attitude which have culminated in this movement. From 1945 to 1960 there was a great deal of faith in science. Science had convincingly demonstrated its strength in winning the war. It was demonstrating its strength in winning, in peace, a richer life for all. From 1961 to 1967, the social impact of science was developed through the application to it of the concepts of systems analysis and economics. From 1967 to the eighties was a phase of disenchantment. Science policy came under attack. The aims of science and of scientists became suspect. A massive questioning of the whole purpose and direction of science began. New issues surfaced, prominent among which were the ways in which science was depriving us of the earth's resources, polluting a pure environment, enmeshing itself in the military and industrial complex, perfecting techniques of political control, and subordinating concepts of privacy and liberty.

The writings of Aldous Huxley[5] and Oswald Spengler,[6] who spoke in pre-war years of the frightening aspects of the new world that science was fashioning and of the impending decline of western civilization, gained new momentum. Post-industrial prophets, such as Lewis Mumford,[7] sounded warnings of the extent to which mankind had permitted itself to be dominated by technology and the machine. Albert Einstein and Bertrand Russell spoke ominously of the cataclysms that science had prepared for mankind.[8] Arthur Koestler[9] and Charles Reich[10] added their voices to the general protest. Journalists such as Daniel Greenberg[11] revealed the machinations that went on in the halls of science, and public interest crusaders such as Ralph Nader[12] showed the way in which science had become subservient to industry. The voices of the new left, fuelled by the Vietnam war, saw science as supporter and tool of a discredited economic and political order. Analysts of the youthful opposition to technocratic society saw in it the only means of averting the dismal despotisms forecast by Huxley and Orwell.[13]

The result was a call to end the free career of science and place it under social control. But scientists reacted loudly, reviving with a new intensity the intellectual debate on scientific freedom and social planning, a debate that went back, through the writings of scientific historians and sociologists in the 1950s and 1960s, to the intellectual discussions of the 1930s and, indeed, back to Marx.

In this debate, scientists such as J. D. Bernal contended that planning and organization should direct science to the satisfaction of rationally anticipated social needs, while others such as Michael Polanyi argued for freedom.[14] The one view leads to participation by scientists in the moving social and political currents of their time, the other to the unfettered pursuit of knowledge by each scientist in the way he or she thinks best.

Lawyers as a group have, perhaps from lack of interest, refrained so far from participating in this debate. They need to join in, for they can bring insights which the scientists and philosophers lack. But they cannot do so on the basis of the law alone. Today's lawyers need to come to grips with the relevant philosophical literature.

Of special value to them in the coming human rights debate on scientific freedom are the criteria formulated by R. K. Merton in 1942.[15] Some of the qualities Merton identified as winning prestige for science were disinterestedness, communism, and universalism. By disinterestedness, Merton meant that the scientists submit their work to fellow scientists who judge its worth by standards of its own, unrelated to the external standards of community appreciation or disapproval, such as political, business or social assessments. Non-scientific criteria are thereby rigidly excluded. This quality, in particular, has become obscured by the present trend to seek funds, recognition, and advancement from sources which have other criteria of evaluation.

By communism Merton meant the sharing of scientific knowledge. A new advance may not be kept locked in the mind of its originator. Present military and industrial secrecy function on a directly antagonistic principle.

By universalism Merton meant standards of evaluation which should operate irrespective of the desires or prescriptions of particular nations, groups, or individuals.

The erosion of these principles has also eroded the prestige of science, although Merton's critics argue that individual scientists can fall away from these norms without in any way affecting the prestige of science. With the loss of objectivity resulting from the pursuit of political and financial power, there has also been a blurring of objectives to the extent that, in certain types of scientific activity, it is difficult to say whether their objective is political, industrial, or scientific.

Genetic engineering, nuclear proliferation, and cybernetic technology have also contributed to the disillusionment with science. Through these developments, the position of the scientist is one of power associated with fear, mistrust, and concern. How scientists emerge from this phase depends on the extent to which they are able to increase their sensitivity and response to their social responsibilities.

Science and the law now speak in such different languages that it is difficult to find a meeting ground between them. This has not always been the case. In seventeenth-century England, when science was part of the knowledge of every gentleman, Chief Justice Hale, the greatest lawyer of his day, was the author of such writings as 'An Essay touching the Gravitation of Fluid Bodies' and 'Observations touching the Torricellian Experiment'. The Royal Society began in the legal chambers of William Ball in the Middle Temple, and several Lord Chancellors were members of this august body. The Inns of Court were conveniently situated near the main centres of London scientific activity, so that scientific lectures could be heard during law terms, and 'a certain amount of familiarity and knowledge could be expected of a young man who wanted to cut a fashionable figure in society'.

It is no longer possible as it was a century ago for the lawyer and the judge to keep abreast of the latest developments in science, however hard they may try. This is not surprising, considering that scientists themselves are narrowing down their specialities to the point where communication between them is difficult.

Although the lay observer may have the impression that a lawyer cross-examining an expert knows more about the subject than the expert, this is an illusion. Science is becoming increasingly inaccessible to the lawyer. No lawyer, lacking a special mathematical training, can seriously contend that he or she feels at home in the rarefied world of quantum mechanics, immunology or computer technology. The same difficulties confront a judge who must make a decision involving some complex scientific question.

Ethics

People of the utmost intelligence and integrity are often carried away by their devotion to work in which they are deeply immersed. When the V2 rockets launched from Peenemünde on 3 October 1942 were successful, a celebration party was held at Peenemünde. When news reached Los Alamos that the atomic bomb it helped create had successfully flattened Hiroshima, there was such jubilation that scientists rushed to telephones to arrange dinner parties at nearby restaurants.[16]

The vast resources of the modern state – and of corporate power – make it possible for thousands of scientists to be employed in some minute area of research to which they would not lend themselves if they knew the total research plan of which their work was a part. The frightening overall picture of such research presents itself only when it is too late for scientists to retract from the venture. Those whose skill went into the making of the first atomic bomb were not all aware of the end to which their overall research was directed. Oppenheimer, the nuclear scientist who helped create the atom bomb, used the words of the *Bhagavad Gita* to confess to a feeling that 'I am become Death, the destroyer of worlds'.

Today, there is a need for an international rather than a national approach to these issues. Scientists often convince themselves that research dangerous to humanity needs nevertheless to be undertaken to strengthen their own countries, thereby achieving a balance of power and thus preserving world peace. A telling answer to this view is the statement of Andrei D. Sakharov, principal member of the scientific team which gave Russia its nuclear weapons and the hydrogen bomb:

When, twenty-five years ago I began working on those horrible weapons, I subjectively thought that this was work for peace – that it was leading to a balance of power, and thus was useful to my people – to some extent – to all mankind.

This was how I felt, and I think this view was shared by many others – the more so since we didn't have any choice at the time.

Today's science is too international to permit its workers any view but the widest possible of their work and of its impact.

Power

Because of the scale of its operations, science has been forced to compromise with wealth and power. 'Big' science needs 'big' money, and such money comes only from those who have political or financial power. Undivided loyalty to pure research is no longer possible in many fields of science. Scientists are caught in a conflict of loyalties – between loyalty to critical inquiry and loyalty to authority – and a strong case exists to 'disestablish' science and free it from the shackles of authority.

The realities of modern power structures make such disestablishment manifestly unattainable and, furthermore, scientists themselves show no unity on the issue. 'Empire building' in science is big business. Nuclear research and the space programme showed the way. The growth of the multinationals and the enormous patronage they wield, and the lavish scale of military expenditure, all combine to produce this result.

Secrecy

Scientists of one government department have been known to preserve secrecy from those of another on a matter which interests them both. A classic example was the competition between the US army and air force in the development of ballistic missiles. Each service withheld information from the other, and General Schriever, from the air force, visiting army installations, was not allowed to be accompanied by the head of the air force programme.[17]

Another example of secrecy was Project Starfish – a test explosion by the US government following research conducted behind intense security. The fear, discounted by the government, that it would produce enough atomic particles to cause persistent changes in the natural Van Allen belts surrounding the globe, was later confirmed. Environmental damage which would require more than thirty years to right itself could have been averted had there been more openness.[18]

Censorship is also used by governments to control scientists. Articles submitted to journals such as *Environmental Protection* and *Nature* have been censored by government departments. A director of an experimental station run by the Nature Conservancy in the UK complained that a paper submitted to him as editor of *Environmental Protection* had been censored to save inconvenience to a government department.[19] An article on the possibility of human liver cancer developing through a fungus growing on peanuts was deleted from the proofs of *Nature* magazine because the British government did not want to upset its relationship with the peanut growing countries of Africa.

In Victoria, under the public service regulations, members of a government department, even scientific employees, cannot divulge to the public the contents of any discussions within the department.

Commercial firms competing in the field of research are even stricter in their secrecy. Ralph Nader[20] has shown how marine pollution resulting from industrial technology proceeds apace under cover of commercial secrecy, despite legal requirements to disclose it.

Many scientists are employed on research for large corporations and their first loyalties, especially in the area of information, are to the corporations.

Scientists often compete among themselves, each anxious

to reach research targets ahead of rivals, especially with increasing numbers vying for limited funds. Peer approval, through the Nobel Prize and other prizes, intensifies this competitive instinct. Where once it was coincidence that Newton and Leibniz were independently working on calculus at the same time, today it is not the exception but the norm that closely parallel endeavours are underway. The secrecy which results also keeps the public ignorant.

Another aspect of scientific secrecy is what may be called 'institutional secrecy': the tendency of the scientific establishment as an institution to keep its activities away from the public. Underlying reasons are the technicality of the subject and the belief that scientific matters are not for lay people, set against a background of an institutional aversion to external interference. The chairman of the Australian Academy of Science Committee, which controls experiments in genetic engineering, for example, was reported as having declined to give details of the experiments in Australia to which his committee had given the go-ahead.[21]

Science has become big business. It spends millions of dollars of public money, and there are so many projects that there is much lobbying and scrambling for funds. The amounts involved are often huge. The 300 GeV CERN proton synchroton in England, for example, was estimated to cost £150 million, and the Concorde has involved over a thousand million pounds. Even at lesser levels funds are scarce and projects are many. Pioneering work in reporting scientific activities to the public has stripped away the myth that science is above politics.[22]

When space scientists were winning funds and public acclaim, some 'earth scientists' decided on a project to draw some of the distinction from their rivals. In a chance conversation in a club, a project to sink a hole into the mantle of the earth, drilling right through the earth's crust, was proposed. This was the abortive Mohole project, which aimed at extracting energy from the earth's mantle.[23] In the words of one of its pioneers, 'This would be the perfect anti-analogue of a space probe. Think of the attention it would attract to the earth sciences.'[24] A technological 'spectacular' is a highly effective method of earning distinction and raising funds on a scale sufficient to confer immense power and prestige on those in charge of it. Whatever the merits or dangers of the Mohole exercise, the incident illustrates another disturbing factor in scientific decision making.

Unethical Use of Science

Scientists rarely pursue their research with deliberately evil intent. With those who use their work, on the other hand, the reverse is often the case. Their interest is in power and profit not knowledge.

Entrenched on the pinnacles of power one often sees people who are prepared to use whatever means are available to keep their positions. Modern technology, from miniaturized surveillance devices to massive data banks, gives such people a range of weapons tailor-made for this purpose. A politician crazed with power may not hesitate to use the most drastic of these devices.

The result is a strange contrast between the dedication of the creators of the technology and the determination and power hunger of those prepared to use it. If this was seen as a danger in the past, it is a danger multiplied a hundredfold today. This dichotomy between the world of the scientist and the world of the politician needs to be grasped by those who press for uninhibited scientific research. Sir Walter Crocker, the Lieutenant-Governor of South Australia, observed, when opening a recent science teachers' conference:

The first unravels the technology while the second stands by prepared to put it to unscrupulous use. Those who vote the second into power, the people, need to be aware of the dimensions of the problem. It is for the first group to alert them. Einstein, Fermi, Oliphant, and the rest unlock the atom: Nixon, Brezhnev, the Hitlers and the rest turn it into bombs, and with half a dozen associates have the power to destroy the world. It is a frightening dichotomy.

The power hungry are not, and never were, confined to politicians. Many other people and groups have sought power for themselves and their organizations without actively participating in the political arena. Commercial organizations, for example, have readily embraced technology as a means of increasing their production, distribution and range of merchandise. In commerce as in politics, the end is used to justify the means, and the pursuit of gain has never permitted considerations of human rights to stand in its way.

Today's conditions highlight this danger, in the context of trading corporations grown so financially powerful as to rival nation states. Their dominance is such that they speak to sovereign governments from a position of strength and sometimes from a position of dominance.

Next to governments and the military establishment, these are the buyers of the new technology. They are the sellers too. The social evil of the wares they sell or the research they induce is small in their eyes when compared to the financial profit. Corporate law gives them a veil of anonymity and privilege. These organizations fund their own research, openly invoking rights to secrecy and openly defying nationally applicable guidelines laid down for research. The recent stand of some corporations in regard to recombinant DNA research is an illustration, for when the nationally applicable US National Institute of Health guidelines were laid down, some corporations refused to conform to them, asserting that the guidelines could bind institute-funded research but not research funded by the corporations.

The extent to which such research dominates academic research is yet to be investigated, but even as early as the 1950s trends were discernible of the influence of the research of corporations on its academic counterpart. According to one study of the influence of business corporations:

. . . every one of the trends to be found in corporation research is to be found in academic research . . . There is the same bent to large team projects, the same bent to highly systematized planning, to committees and programmes. Like his brother in management, the scientist is becoming our organisation man.[25]

These buyers of scientific research are often in league with the military establishment from whom they receive their contracts. The combination operates at such a level of power that individual scientists pursuing research according to the ideals of their profession are small fry, readily discarded.

Institutions of learning themselves are often dependent for some of their scientific research on grants handed out by these corporations. In the US, grants from the military establishment of several million dollars have kept scientific research schools going. Here, as elsewhere, the old adage that the one who pays the piper calls the tune must apply. Government money has not only added to ordinary university research, it has altered its whole structure. The problem has become so acute in the US that a sociologist commented:

As the universities have accepted more research contracts, they have relinquished control over the direction of research. The government sets the tune; committees responsible to it specify the problems, pass on the work, and appoint the personnel. The universities provide the setting and the essential housekeeping services. University scientists still do most of the research, but increasingly the allegiance of many is to the 'research centre', a quasi-academic institution which draws its heat and light from the university, its directions from elsewhere.[26]

Increasingly, universities are beginning to assert their right to determine what research will go on within their walls. But the resistance, taken over all, is feeble and belated. Fortunately, the Australian universities are as yet free of this dominance.

The terrorist organizations, which sometimes have the backing of governments, are also in the market. No suffering inflicted by them is too great, no price paid for weaponry is too high. With nuclear, chemical, and biological technology of current destructive power available comparatively inexpensively, their arsenals have grown immensely. Legal control over the availability to them of the most dangerous technology is already minimal.

In the developed countries, organized crime is often big business, rivalling orthodox power centres in influence and political 'clout'. It functions both underground and under a veil of corporate respectability, for the money made in crime is often channelled into apparently honest businesses. Science for organized crime is a toy to be bought and used for maximum profit.

It is idle to dismiss, as some scientists do, the *application* of technology as being in an area over which scientists have no control and therefore no responsibility. It is a fact of life that technology once discovered does not halt within the enclaves of science. The dichotomy between the creator and the user of technology is one of the problems at the heart of modern scientific research.

Chapter 9

Academic Freedom and the Law

Freedom to pursue and disseminate knowledge evolved in the context of freedom of expression. But we can no longer afford to give science a free hand in the name of freedom of inquiry. The concept must be rethought. Free trade was treated as a right until it was realized that there was a limit to the earth's resources. Freedom to discharge waste into the oceans was unlimited until this century. No amount of freedom of speech entitles a person to shout 'Fire!' in a crowded theatre, as Justice Holmes observed. There is no absolute right of freedom of scientific research. Each principle can only be viewed in the context of its time.

The limits set in certain branches of science must force us to consider whether freedom of scientific inquiry is a right or only a privilege granted to the scientist under certain conditions. According to one view, if we surrender total scientific freedom, we surrender totally scientific freedom. This is a fallacy. Every principle needs constant surveillance, and just as constant vigilance is the price we pay for democracy, so is vigilance the price we pay for the benefits of science. Some scientists must surrender some freedom of research to society in the public interest. 'Society' here is not synonymous with the scientific establishment, which would be inappropriate to control such research. The final arbiter of scientific research must be society, not the scientist.

Common law considers every principle, however sweeping, in its factual context. By slow degrees, exceptions and new interpretations modify the principle and indeed sometimes show it in an altogether different light. That is how the common law has survived without becoming inflexible. There is no reason to think that any other approach can be adopted towards the principle of freedom of scientific research.

Moral Accountability

The belief that science and progress went hand in hand meant that the question of the scientist's moral accountability for the consequences of his research received scarcely any serious attention until World War II.

Two events of the war more than any others made the first major inroads on this complacent assumption. The experiments conducted by medical scientists in the concentration camps and the responsibility of scientists for the creation of the atomic bomb brought home as never before that science was not always an altruistic pursuit and that the question of the moral responsibility of the scientist was deserving of the most serious attention.

If scientists know and foresee the consequences of their research as, for example, scientists working on the atom bomb knew the purposes for which their skills were being used, are they morally responsible? Could they escape such responsibility on the basis that they are engaged in the academic pursuit of knowledge, and argue that it was politicians who put their knowledge to destructive uses?

Scientists often reach a point in their research where they can anticipate that the knowledge they will unravel will be capable of use for irreversible and destructive purposes. It is naive to expect that knowledge of great commercial or military value will be left unused. A dilemma arises, however, when the scientist can see that the same discovery has the potential to be used at once for immensely harmful and immensely beneficial purposes. Nuclear irradiation, for example, can be used for atomic weapons *as well as peaceful purposes*.

Scientists have no clear guidelines about how to proceed. If they know that their knowledge will be used against mankind, their position is not any different from that of ordinary people who, in the law of tort or crime, are held responsible for the foreseen and foreseeable consequences of their acts. Lord Rutherford, who believed that anyone who spoke of extracting power from the atom was talking moonshine, obviously did not know that his research could be used for destructive purposes and was, by this standard, exempt.

What distinguishes the moral responsibility of scientists

and ordinary people? That scientists are acting in the pursuit of knowledge is inadequate as an exculpatory ground. The related argument, that they do not intend to use their knowledge for damaging purposes, does not bear examination if the results are clearly foreseeable. A stronger argument exists in cases where scientists are unaware of the purposes for which their research is needed. This often occurs in the context of military or commercial research, where a scientist working on some small segment of a large programme is kept in ignorance of its overall purpose. Another circumstance which may mitigate moral culpability exists when scientists are completely under the control of powerful employers, for example, the state or a corporation, which can dismiss them if they refuse to proceed. Superior orders ought not, however, to exonerate scientists completely. The law must give leadership in this field by formulating concepts of responsibility. The jurist, Julius Stone, in formulating a standard of ethical responsibility, said:

Unless then, we indulge a belief in such a miraculous transformation of the known world, we must attribute moral responsibility to those who, after they realised that their work would lead 'almost inevitably' to nuclear weapons, nevertheless continued on this path.[1]

Such a moral concept once formulated and accepted will lead to the formulation of legal rules, but no legal rules will evolve in the absence of such a moral concept.

Legal Accountability
The scientific establishment is free from any sorts of checks or balances. Public servants are controlled by public authority, and nearly all the professions – except perhaps the clergy – pursue their activities in contact with a public whose favour or disapproval determines what will be allowed. Science is a power centre within the state, of awesome and unprecedented potential. It is contrary to all democratic principle that such a concentration of power should be free of public control.

Nearly every group of skilled people organized in professions is in a direct contractual relationship with the public. Architects, surveyors, engineers, chemists, doctors, and accountants contract with the public for the provision of their skilled services. The contract operates as a determinant and a check. Scientists pursuing knowledge in their laboratories have no such contractual relationships.

Scientists have so far viewed themselves as immune from the consequences of their work on just this basis, that they have no direct contact, and that accountability was inconceivable in the context of the widely held traditional belief that the advancement of pure knowledge is always only beneficial.

If moral responsibility can be brought home to scientists for results which they could (or should) have foreseen, the transition to legal responsibility is not difficult. Indeed, there are some principles in the common law that help to bridge the gap.

If a woman, for example, who knows full well that there are children playing in the street, leaves her car in their midst on an incline with the doors unlocked and only the handbrake on, she must know that a foreseeable and indeed probable consequence is that one of the children may climb into the car and release the brake, causing damage and injury. There are legal principles based on negligence which are adequate to establish legal liability in such a situation. A scientist, who puts together the chemical components of a spray, which he knows will be used by the public, if aware that it will probably produce genetic defects in the offspring of the users, is not in a very different position. Damage is a foreseeable and probable consequence of his act. He may be screened, in the law of contract, by his employer who alone may have a direct relationship with the purchaser. The law of tort, however, which imposes a general duty, irrespective of contract, on all who are reasonably within the circle of dangers resulting from one's act, is adequate to establish the scientist's liability.

Two decisions in the common law must not be lost sight of by scientists who feel that their isolation from the public gives them protection.

In 1932, Lord Atkin, in the British House of Lords, had to decide whether a consumer had an action against the manufacturer of a bottle of ginger beer containing a dead snail which caused shock and injury to her health. The legal difficulty was that this consumer had not bought the ginger beer from the manufacturer, but was consuming it in a cafe, so that there was no contractual relationship between the two. Lord Atkin, realizing the importance of imposing on the manufacturer a duty of care towards those who could be expected to use his product, worked out such a principle: if a person is 'within the ambit of those who ought reasonably to have been in contemplation as being affected by an act' the doer is responsible, irrespective of contract.[2]

Another distinguished judge, Lord Blackburn, had laid down a crucial principle in 1866. In this case, a person, who for purposes of his own, had dammed up a large quantity of water on his premises, was held liable to make good the damage to his neighbour which resulted from the escape of that water, irrespective of whether he had been negligent or not. The basis of the decision was that if one brings dangerous substances onto one's premises, one must take responsibility for damage caused by their escape, however it is caused.[3]

In nuclear plants and recombinant DNA experimentation, scientists bring to premises substances that were not naturally there. Since their escape, however carefully guarded against, can cause untold harm to people, the scientists are liable even if they have taken the utmost precautions. Law Professor Ronald Dworkin, at the Asilomar Conference on recombinant DNA experimentation in 1975, told assembled scientists that, whatever the immunities they might claim, it was eventually by a lay jury and a lay judge that questions of their liability would be determined. The scientist would be exonerated, perhaps, by other scientists, but it would not be a panel of scientists who would sit in judgment. Academic freedom and freedom of inquiry are not as yet defences in law, and ought not to be, for freedom of inquiry, though a valuable right, is not an absolute one. There are other freedoms and rights to be balanced against them.

Chapter 10
Inadequate Political Structures

The political effects of technology need no elaboration. Whether we look at the break up of the old social stratifications through the industrial revolution, or the increase of elderly and dependent groups caused by modern medical technology, the techno-political impact is profound.

The Dominance of Technology
Political institutions moulded to the needs of the society in which they operate will change as the values in that society change. But the rate of change resulting from technology is now too fast for these institutions to keep up. Some theoreticians argue that technological change, not ideological conflict or economics, is a prime factor in producing political crises.

The adjustments necessary will not always guarantee peace, but the longer they are delayed, the more violent and troubled the process will be.

Technology achieves much of its strength through functioning hand in glove with commerce. In a society dominated by wealth and materialism, whatever tends to increase wealth is sought after and obscures other considerations and values. The corporate state founded on this value system is relentlessly single-minded, and only recognizes the values of technology, organization, efficiency, growth, progress.[1] Nothing short of a revision of attitudes and a new way of life based on other values can bring about change.

Herbert Marcuse, an analyst of the predicament of people in modern industrial society, argues that the comforts of the technological society mask the inroads that technology makes on freedom; and political systems, reinforced by the technological means available to them, eventually degenerate into a form of authoritarianism.[2]

Lewis Mumford identifies the pursuit of progress, profit, productivity, property and publicity, all of them wedded to technology and the machine, as the five major ills in our society. As long as society remains wedded to the ideology of the machine, he argues, a cultural, ecological and personal desert will stretch out ahead of us, in both capitalist and communist countries.[3]

A similar philosophy underlies the British economist Schumacher's plea that the waste engendered by technological society and the human misery this creates be reversed by a return to a simpler way of life.[4]

Technology not only dominates politics, it also shapes nearly all attitudes and patterns of conduct. Technology sets the life of modern people in an atmosphere of waste which promotes further waste, which in its turn feeds the technological and commercial machine. Political life and political decision making become geared to this wasteful way of life.[5] It is one of the possible causes of world conflict and hence of the end of civilization.

The speed of technological change has left social and political institutions unprepared. Western countries, the US in particular, by permitting technology to lead rather than be led, are producing steadily worsening waste. Eventually these forces will close in on western political systems, and they will be unable to deal adequately with them without recourse to the ideology and methodology of authoritarianism.[6]

If the freedoms taken for granted in a liberal democracy can be submerged under pressure from technology, it will be an indictment of our generation because, on every side, the dangers are clear.

When one comes to consider international implications, one must confront the growing gulf between the rich and the poor nations, which technology has produced and which it furthers. If the benefits of technology are not shared, the demands of the underprivileged may erupt in a burst of violence and destruction. Conferences such as the Law of the Sea Conference have so far failed to reach accord on some of the most fundamental issues, because those countries with the technology are anxious to use it to exploit the riches of the sea bed before the countries without it develop the necessary technology to obtain their fair share. In the same way, the technology available to multi-national corporations enables them to continue the economic and political victimization of the poor.

As we move into the future, we must ask ourselves not how this problem was solved before, but how it must be solved in the future. The forward perspective takes the place of the backward glance, and the book of precedents gives place to the chart of projections. At least for the next generation or two, this dominance of the future must continue.

Not all writers view with gloom the technological impact on politics. Some see distinct advantages to the political process in the new technology. The broadening of political participation,[7] the splintering of society into more articulate groups,[8] and a spirit of buoyant optimism[9] are among the more hopeful views.

Daniel Bell, a seminal writer in this field, does not see technology overriding politics. He notes the dramatic shift to knowledge as the new basis of power.[10] Scientists, in his view, become dominant figures in the new society. He believes that despite technology, the setting of goals will remain a political process, as the politician, not the technocrat, will be the ultimate holder of power.[11] The US sociologist, Brzezinski, while observing that the numerous technical means of controlling people build up the danger of a dictatorship, believes that modern societies contain built-in protections, one of which is that the community is better alerted by its intellectuals to respond to change.[12] Others are hopeful that society will be able to adjust by an improvement in its mechanisms. Lawyers see this as achievable through constitutional change.[13] Alvin Toffler, the futurist, sees hope in institutions that can overcome the preoccupation of current legislatures with the next election.

But through all these writers' works there flows a feeling of unease. The temptation to gain organizational efficiency always beckons in the direction of more technology, and more technology means more control and less freedom.[14]

Capitalism's traditional reliance on supply and demand as

a means of regulating the distribution of the social product has been eroded by the complexity of technology. Some housewives, for example, use aerosol sprays without understanding their potential pollution, and some farmers use fertilizers despite the danger of developing skin cancer from its nitrogen content. The factors that should govern consumer choice are no longer within the consumer's ability to see or evaluate.

Just as in time of war, consumer preference is suspended and an extraneous judgment takes over the decision on what goods should be produced, so in the age of technology an external judgment will need to determine this. Some private industrial research needs government subsidization, and some research needs control or prohibition. The planner dethrones the public. The old concept of freedom and laissez faire yields to the new concept of planning and control. As technology intensifies and spreads, so the old market mechanism becomes increasingly unable to handle it.

The technological complexity of the decisions results in most of them being made by scientists. In this respect, science has become society's legislature, displacing market preference and government policy. The scientist cannot be permitted to monopolize this area of decision making.

Hand in hand with this development is a transformation in the role of business. Formerly it was accountable to none but itself and the market. Today it is also accountable to governments. It once mattered little whether cobbler John or farrier Bill dismissed his paid hands or put his shutters down. It is a matter of public concern today if BHP or Comalco lay off 5,000 workers or close down a factory around which a township has developed. Likewise, the quality of a product, whether it is a car or a telephone service, is no longer a private matter between producer and consumer; it also concerns the government and the community. The need for external regulation thus becomes increasingly felt, and the public intrusion into the 'private' sector acquires a new dimension.

The dangers and the opportunities inherent in these developments need constitutional planning if the former are to be avoided and the latter put to fuller service in the interests of society.

The dazzling achievements of technology and the abundance of material goods it produces have epitomized human progress, which in turn is judged by the growth rate in the national product; other human values, important in earlier centuries, have been discarded. It was only in the mid seventies that the notion of the quality of life rather than the level of production and wealth came to be recognized as a means of judging a country's general level of attainment.

The result, in political terms, is that attention tends to be diverted from the political malaise enveloping most countries to a sense of satisfaction at the increase in consumer goods and in the general level of material prosperity.

Power Shifts
The technological age has also produced some remarkable power shifts to which the political process has not yet attuned itself. Foremost among the concentrations of power it has helped to produce are the multi-national corporations. It is technology that has given them the knowledge and organizational skills for spreading out globally. Without the computer, in particular, this phenomenon would not have occurred.

When these corporations find a common interest with government departments, as for example in the execution of military contracts, the coalescence of power is too great for democratic processes to handle. They can dictate terms to governments around the world. Their political power comes not only from their financial power and sophisticated technology but also from the tens of thousands of jobs they provide. Nothing can control them because, in the last analysis, they are dominated by a mandateless élitist minority.

Indeed, through their association with government, these corporations almost assume the status of government agencies. A corporation working on some secret weapon in a defence contract, for example, acquires all the aura and authority of government and the military. Its leaders move in and out of the precincts of power with a facility which makes them part and parcel of the governmental process. The border between government authority and private enterprise is blurred, and although the two have come together in fact, private enterprise has the advantage of being treated as separate in theory. Nor is the public interest helped by the growing interchange of personnel between the two. The corporate world attracts the most senior staff from government departments and agencies, and as they move from one realm to the other they take with them the confidential information that they have acquired in their capacity as trustees for the public. In all industrialized countries, this sinister traffic is increasing, and although the general public sees government and corporate employees as being in a bargaining relationship, their secret interlockings pass unnoticed.

In all this, there has been a shift in power to some branches of industry. Media and computer industries are some of these. Petro-chemicals, nuclear physics, aerospace, communications, electronics are others. Why power centres on these industries is an interesting question. The power they have is often markedly political, however, and our political apparatuses have not taken note of their privileged position, treating alike all industry whether textiles or nuclear technology.

Among other power shifts is the shift of power to technocrats. Although not superior in learning to the linguist or the humanist, technocrats have power incommensurate with their peers. Superior in mobility, remuneration and privilege, they are rapidly forming a new élite.

Inadequate Public Representation

Decisions of major importance involving the use of technology are often taken at the highest legislative and executive levels, to which the public interest campaigner has limited access. Public interest groups find their energies dissipated by facing a multitude of issues without adequate concentration or background work on any one. The staying power of the former is greater, for enormous funds lie behind the front-line campaigners. Expenses involved in lobbying become tax deductible. The expertise of the more influential lobbyists in the land is available for a fee which the public interest groups can rarely command. The battle is an unequal one and, as between the citizen and some socially damaging technological innovation, the citizen must lose.

In the US, the power of lobbyists has grown to such proportions as to touch off speculation that it is they who run the country.[15] The killing of such socially beneficial measures as a consumer protection agency, hospital cost containment, and the crude oil tax in the energy bill are directly attributable to private lobbying, and the once influential public interest lobbies are losing ground.

Society, which supports and is affected by science, has also the right to govern science. Where formerly science and technology could follow any course they pleased, in the future the process must be reversed.

The direction of scientific research belongs as much to society and its representatives as to the scientists, and the two should act in partnership. Indeed, neither laymen nor lawyers should fear the technicalities involved, for when properly supplied with the facts they are by no means incompetent to reach a commonsense decision on whether a given piece of research is socially dangerous or not. Memorable examples exist of scientists being in serious error on purely scientific matters. When Mesmer put forward his theory of hypnotism, for example, he was ostracized by the scientific community and stigmatized as an imposter. Professor Langley of the Smithsonian Institute, who envisaged that the recently invented internal combustion engine could be used to propel flying machines, was expelled from the institute. Professor Simon Newcomb was able to prove mathematically to the satisfaction of his fellow scientists that a flying machine that was heavier than air was mathematically impossible and only a visionary's dream.[16]

All this suggests that scientific opinion, like all human opinion, is fallible, and as far as its social effect is concerned, the scientist can often be an erroneous guide, as Rutherford was, when he said that whoever talked of extracting power from the atom was talking moonshine.

Hopeful recent indications of citizen involvement come from the spheres of recombinant DNA and nuclear energy. In the first of these, a citizen's committee in Boston in 1976 threw away traditional lay restraints and inquired with much competence into the complex problems of recombinant DNA. The way in which lay interest has been aroused in the uranium and nuclear energy debates of the past few years is also a useful index of the extent of possible lay participation.

Political institutions that were adequate until the mid twentieth century are inadequate now and will be anomalies tomorrow; and even if they were geared to the needs of today, the speed of change is such that additional mechanisms will be required. We need, therefore, to anticipate and design our systems for the future.[17]

In 1933, the eminent British engineer, Sir Alfred Ewing, suggested that there should be a moratorium on inventions in order to take stock of existing ones which had not been assimilated. Although he was 'hooted as a crank', subsequent events have led us to conclude that Sir Alfred's warning deserved more attention.[18]

In assessing future technology and making the socio-political decisions connected with it, society needs to formulate its goals.[19] Clearly, goals should not be dictated from the top but must come from the community.

There is a heavy responsibility on lawyers and institutions of legal learning to revamp their thinking and their training to the age of technology – a long overdue task to which their best efforts must urgently be directed.

Chapter 11

Agenda for Action

The effect of technology on human rights must give concerned people cause for disquiet.

A number of suggestions are contained in this chapter, involving changes of structure, attitudes, and procedures. They will not be appropriate for every society and situation, but they deserve consideration if we are to face the future with confidence. Not all of them are intended to be adopted simultaneously. They offer a range of choices from which a selection needs to be made.

Technology Classification Committees
Only a small proportion of scientific research poses real dangers; most of it will prove to be innocuous. A classification committee could identify the projects that are potentially harmful and of doubtful value and alert the public to the dangers.

Technology Assessment Boards
Technology assessment is the informed examination of the effect of a particular development in technology. Its purpose is to clarify policy and set out options so that intelligent choices can be made by responsible public and private decision makers. It should provide early warning systems.

In 1967, in the US, a bill was introduced to establish a technology assessment board, which resulted in the passage of legislation in 1972, creating an Office of Technology Assessment which was to report to the US Congress.

The objectives of the Office of Technology Assessment[1] include identifying existing or probable effects of technology and alternative technological methods and programmes, presenting findings to the appropriate legislative authorities, and identifying areas where additional research is needed.[2]

Technical Hazards Boards
Representatives from technical hazards boards will appear before the legislature as lobbyists against schemes which involve potential risks. Public servants with the requisite scientific background would be employed by the board as full-time researchers and legislation would guarantee the board's right to be heard by the legislature or its committees.

This machinery can in a sense be likened to the opposition in government which keeps Westminster-style democracy alive.

Futures Scanning Agencies in Government Departments
A futures scanning agency in every government department as well as a government department exclusively devoted to the scanning of futures should be set up. Any technological measure of social importance should need clearance from this department. Staff working for the futures department should be protected constitutionally from victimization lest their advice does not please the government. The department should have close contact with the public in a consulting and educating role.

An example of a measure designed on these lines is HR988, the 'foresight provision', in the US House of Representatives, which requires that standing committees engage in futures research and long-term analysis.

Committees for Alternative Futures
Forecasting the future involves not only passive predictions about the direction in which technology is taking us, but also active choices between alternatives. Committees need to map out these alternatives in detail, and bring them before the public and the legislature to enable informed decisions to be taken.

Many other methods are possible for increasing 'anticipatory' democracy. Among them are citizens grouped together in '2000' organizations, community action programmes, discussion groups in schools, Lions, Apex, Rotary, YMCA, Red Cross and other service groups, futures resource centres, and futures-oriented primers for schoolchildren.[3]

Centres for the Study of Scientific Policy
Not all countries have a ministry that is responsible for scientific policy, and where they do exist, scientific policy tends to be confused with the political policies of the government in power. Any presentation to the public of the technology relevant to some governmental programme runs the risk of being slanted to fit into the government's plan. It is important that impartial committees, guaranteed independence by law, make it their business to research governmental scientific policy and point out possible alternatives and flaws.

This involves a constitutional question. The constitutional position of science may vary from country to country depending on the interpretation placed by its courts on questions of freedom of speech and thought and belief.[4] In the US, the constitutional position of science has been moulded by a series of decisions giving science an affirmative and protected status.

Centres for Integrating Technology with National Goals
The short-term perspectives of traditional political structures make them unsuitable for formulating a country's national goals, and expert committees are needed, such as the National Goals Research Staff appointed by President Nixon or the high-powered commission appointed by President Eisenhower, which reported on goals for Americans. Once these committees put forward their proposals, studies must be launched to see in what way technology can be used to achieve them.[5]

Professional Futurists
With the evolution of university courses on futures, expert futurists will be trained as professionals to advise on futures.

A high ethical standard enforced among them should prevent them from reporting on projects in a manner calculated to please their clients. They need the same degree of detachment as is required of futures departments. It should be set down by statute that any major project involving technology should be accompanied by a report from a registered futurist. Years of experience in technology assessment should be a prerequisite for registration as a futures expert.

University Committees
Universities should set up committees to study the future. More especially, science and law faculties need to set up futures committees to survey the direction in which their disciplines are going and their adequacy to meet the needs of the future. These committees would be specially effective as universities are both repositories of information and agencies of research.

Through the committees, universities need to guard against being lured by the funds, power, and prestige of powerful sponsors – whether military or commercial – into undertaking research which runs counter to their ideals. Provisions to this end may need to be built into university statutes and research contracts.

Committees of the Bar
The bar has been insufficiently used as a source of guidance and direction. Sub-committees of science-oriented members of the bar could be set up to keep an eye on the challenges posed by science. The impact on the law of each minor scientific development must be kept under scrutiny and reported back to the bar for appropriate action.[6]

The establishment of the Standing Committee on Law and Technology of the American Bar Association is a step in this direction as is its quarterly review, *The Jurimetrics Journal.*

Science Commissions
Like a law reform commission, a science commission is needed to issue annual reports on the state of science in a

country, and compel scientists to acknowledge their
responsibility to their society by acting as public watchdogs.
Its composition would ideally be interdisciplinary and non-
political, with legal and scientific members being statutorily
required. Its annual report should be one of the most important documents on public welfare.

Structures for Accountability in Science

Public safety, education, health, housing, freedom of
expression, thought and belief, privacy, cultural pursuits,
family security, and leisure are important factors in social
welfare, often forgotten in the preoccupation with economic
benefits. A true social accounting on any scientific development must take note of its effect in all these fields.

A structure to audit various scientific activities could be
set up and a social auditor-general appointed, who would
issue a regular report to the general public. In business and
company law, progressive writers[7] have mooted the notion
that every company should submit to an annual social audit
in the same way that it submits to an annual financial audit.

Reviving Hidden Technology

There are many technologies of potential value to society
which are not developed because there is little or no private
profit to be made from them. Not all socially useful inventions reach the market, just as not all socially useful technology benefits the public. These agencies could research
such areas and rediscover such hidden technology. The
motor industry, for example, has often shelved technologies
that might prove useful to the public but damaging to its
business interests.

Insurance Mechanisms

Many of the technology related public risks carry no
adequate insurance cover. A general state insurance system
is needed which will automatically compensate the victims
of technology, through, for example, pollution or exposure

to dangerous chemicals. The polluter-pays principle used in Japan to meet claims such as those from Minamata sickness is useful here, but the resources of the polluter may be inadequate to meet the number and size of the claims. In the nuclear industry, for example, claims for damage from a leaking reactor would run to thousands of millions of dollars; there are no private insurance schemes capable of dealing with claims of this size.

Legislative Restructuring

An increasing amount of the legislation of the future will be science related. Legislatures do not have the time or the expertise to come to grips with the complicated technological issues which they need to consider before passing laws.

● A council could be formed from among the ranks of distinguished scientists to advise the legislature.

● A house of scientists could be established as an adjunct to the legislature, and a chamber of scientists elected from the ranks of scientists by scientists themselves.[8] This body could be given limited legislative status and have powers of discussion and debate. A scientific measure would have to pass through this legislative house.

● Legislative sub-committees could be formed of science-oriented legislators who would make it their special responsibility to look into science-oriented pieces of legislation and inform the house of their views.

● A certificate from the technology assessment board could be required legislatively to accompany every bill involving science which is placed before the house.

● When any major science-oriented bill is presented, there should be procedures to allow a public debate on the social consequences.

● A given number of members of the public or of the legislature should have the right to call for an open debate on the scientific implications of a measure before the legislature.

● Where there are competing claims for a share of the public funds allocated to science, the public should be kept informed of the reasons for the eventual allocation. For this purpose, a detailed statement of social objectives should accompany every major allocation.

● The recognized scientific bodies should have an automatic right of audience before the legislature on legislation that is in their field.

Judicial Restructuring

Along with legislative restructuring, there must be a restructuring of the judiciary. Judges untrained in science lack the expertise to decide scientific disputes. It may be necessary to set up a scientific division of the judiciary to which would be appointed only those judges who had combined a scientific background with their legal training. These tribunals would also have lay advisers to help them. The suggestion of establishing a science court manned by a panel of scientist/lawyer judges was made in 1967 in the US, and received strong, if qualified support from the ranks of the judiciary.[9]

Scientific Research Arm of the Judiciary

All divisions of the judiciary need the help of a scientific research arm to provide basic information and scientific expertise. The judicial research arm of the Japanese Supreme Court is a prototype, because it provides the judges, not themselves expert in all departments of law and law-related areas, with the necessary research back-up by specialists. In the same way, it will be possible for a scientific research arm of the judiciary to arm the judges with the necessary scientific data.

Such a judicial research arm could be set up as an ancillary organ of the court structure, to be drawn upon by judges of any section of the judiciary who may need this kind of technical information.

Executive Restructuring

Many suggestions can be made in this field.

● A network of scientific research units could be attached to various ministries, which would be co-ordinated through a central bureau of scientific research.

● A pool of highly skilled bureaucrats with an interdisciplinary science/administration background could be set up.

● Secrecy provisions which many governments impose upon their scientific staff should be removed. Requirements of defence and public safety will, of course, limit the scope of this principle.

● Barriers which compartmentalize scientific work in government departments should be broken down.

● Scientific research of all sorts conducted within various government departments should be reported to a central body.

● Futures sections should be set up in all scientific departments.

A New Administrative Jurisprudence

A new administrative jurisprudence for science will need to be evolved, containing attitudinal, conceptual, and procedural innovations.

The world shortage of raw materials may, by the close of the century, result in highly regimented forms of government strictly controlling the expenditure of natural resources.[10] There will be a plethora of administrative decisions involving the use of raw materials and the grant or refusal of permits, and it will be necessary for new structures to be evolved to survey these licensing procedures and ensure that individual rights are not subsumed in bureaucratic excesses.

Bodies such as environmental protection councils, technology assessment boards and science commissions must be given independence from political pressures.

International Covenants and Treaties

To lend effectiveness to the internal regulation of science-related activities, an increasing number of international covenants and treaties will need to be entered into in many fields, such as DNA experimentation, organ transplants, chemical testing, psychosurgery, data protection, and health regulations. It will also be necessary for an international organization to be set up to issue warning signals when crises are reached in scientific research. There will also be a need for a constitutional provision building such international agreements into national law.

The idea of a world council of scientists with powers of control over science voted to it by the world community may come about in a modified form such as an advisory body whose opinion the world community would treat with great regard.

Links between International and National Bodies

There is often lack of communication between international and national bodies working in the same field. An example is the case of the Human Rights Commission which for many years has been working intensively on the effect of science on human rights but in comparative isolation from similarly oriented university and national bodies. The absence of any entity for establishing such liaison results in much duplication and waste.

In the human rights field, journals such as *Internet* bring to human rights workers news of similar activities in every country. A journal similar to *Internet* is required in the field of science and human rights.

International Technology Assessment Boards and Technical Hazards Boards

These are the international counterparts of the national bodies that have been suggested earlier. The first of these bodies, the International Society for Technological Assessment, was set up in 1973.

An International Code of Conduct on the Transfer of Technology

An internationally recognized code of conduct on the transfer of technology needs to acknowledge that technology is a part of the human heritage. As such, it is a body of knowledge to which all countries should have the right of access. To withhold technology is to refuse to use the resources of the community to improve the living standards of its members.

The interests of all countries, developed and developing alike, demand a recognition that there can be no private empires in the realm of scientific knowledge. The code needs to embody a statement on the lines of the declaration adopted at the sixth special session of the general assembly on the establishment of a new international economic order. Paragraph 4P of this declaration sets out a principle giving the developing countries access to the achievements of modern science and technology, promoting the transfer of technology, and creating an indigenous technology for the benefit of the developing countries in forms and procedures suited to their economies.

Restrictive business practices in transactions involving the transfer of technology need the most careful scrutiny and the technology supplier must likewise be protected.

The Brandt Report[11] points out that barely 1 per cent of spending on research and development in the developed countries is specifically concerned with the problems of the developing countries, while 51 per cent is devoted to defence; that the corporations involved in bringing technology to the developing countries have sales ($830 thousand million) which are equal to the gross national product of all the developing countries excluding oil-exporting developing countries, and that 97 per cent of the world's research takes place in the developed countries.

The report makes many suggestions for the transfer of more technology and shows how dangers threatening our children and grandchildren can be averted, among other things, by a sharing of technology. It also refers to possible revisions in the Paris Convention on intellectual property and patent rights, securing greater recognition by patent holders of the public interest in developing countries, for example, by limiting the duration of patents. The World Intellectual Property Organization and the United Nations

Committee on Trade and Development are working on these aspects.

A Scientific Ombudsman

A high-ranking appointment is needed at a national level of a scientist-lawyer as science ombudsman. Sometimes scientists working for a corporation, university or a government department are required to participate in research which they consider morally objectionable. Such employees may be unable to register their protest without losing employment or promotion prospects. They may already have been victimized for doing so. They need a source of protection.

Expanding the Scientific Ethic

The primary ethical responsibility of the scientist is his or her loyalty to truth. The greatest scientific crime is the distortion of results, and the greatest obligation is accurate reporting of results.

This ethic might have been sufficient in earlier ages, but as danger grew from scientific research, so did the ethical responsibility of the scientist. The scientific community must realize the inadequacies of its traditional ethic and work on developing a broader one.

Ethical Codes for Scientists

The idea of an ethic for science goes all the way back to Francis Bacon. In his work, New Atlantis, scientists took an oath of secrecy for concealing inventions and experiences which they thought fit to keep secret. Between Bacon's age and the post-war twentieth century, little has intervened to create an ethical code for science.

It was against this ethical void that Bertrand Russell and Albert Einstein outlined in 1955 the risks of themonuclear war.[12]

The formulation of ethical codes which will say what is 'right' and 'wrong' from the standpoint of research will be difficult and will suffer in their initial stages from being too general and vague. Broad formulations, however, are a useful start, and they will be refined with experience and with each ruling. Doctors, engineers, and computer scientists have worked out brief ethical codes for themselves. These need to be expanded and refined. All scientists should be brought within the operation of ethical codes.

Societies for Social Responsibility

Societies for social responsibility in science have been formed in many countries following the lead given by scientific groups in the US. An early sign of a developing sense of responsibility in scientists was the one-day strike in March 1969 by faculty members of the Massachusetts Institute of Technology and other US universities protesting against the abuses of science for purposes of war. Another sign is the proposal that practitioners of some branches of science should take oaths to be of service to the public and to place service above self.[13]

Under the impetus provided by such societies, scientists are beginning to see implications of their work to which they had been insensitive before.

Obligatory Codes of Practice

Obligatory codes of practice should develop out of the social concern of the scientific community, but scientists have so far not shown any willingness to adopt such codes. In the field of recombinant DNA experimentation, when US scientists announced their intentions to set up a voluntary code of practice, early in 1982, several city and state legislatures expressed unwillingness to accept procedures which were only voluntary, and threatened to impose stringent regulations unless the guidelines adopted were mandatory.[14] This lack of confidence was heightened by the ambitious plans of the genetic engineering industry which would not necessarily permit its scientists the freedom to observe the voluntary rules. Indeed, in California, the home of genetic engineering research, the state assembly's health committee threatened legislation if the guidelines were not made obligatory.

Clearly, the scientific community needs to build up public confidence not merely by proposing voluntary codes when under pressure but by resorting to them out of an ethical sense even in the absence of public pressures.

Self-imposed Moratoriums

In 1974, a group of leading molecular biologists in the US called for a world-wide moratorium on certain kinds of experiment in molecular genetics. In renouncing the experiments in their own laboratories, scientists had the support of the US National Academy of Sciences and of the vast and powerful National Institute of Health. In the UK, the Medical Research Council issued instructions to its laboratories to observe the ban. The president of the association, Sir John Kendrew, announced his support of the moratorium. A meeting of scientists at Asilomar, California, in 1977, considered and assessed the arguments on either side for restraints in recombinant DNA research, and produced an impressive set of safeguards.

But there are many obstacles to self-restraint. Narrow disciplinary backgrounds and self-interest combine with the lack of ethical values in existing professional training (apart from medicine) to prevent such trends.

Court-imposed Moratoriums

A legal principle needs to be worked out by which the public or a representative body of them is able to petition the court for a moratorium on scientific activity, where the scientists are unwilling to adopt one themselves. The procedural and conceptual aspects would need careful legal study.

Referendums

From time to time, science-related issues, such as nuclear weapons and fluoridation, attract public attention. There are a number of other areas on which the opinion of the public needs to be sought by referendums in view of their profound impact on society. Experimentation with foetal material, in vitro fertilization, and the release of fluorocarbons are some of these.

A prerequisite to such referendums is the construction of machinery for involving the public in scientific debate. Lawyers, scientists, and administrators need to pool their expertise to plan this structure. One procedure, tried out in the Austrian nuclear debate in 1977-78, was to present panels of experts and lay people on television. Viewers joined in their discussions through a telephone network.

After the questioning of scientific experts, a referendum was held to obtain the views of the public on the policy questions involved. Constitutional provisions are needed to make a consideration of this view of the public binding upon the legislature.

Plebiscites on the Future
Public participation in government should not be restricted to the short-term political issues of election time. This inherent weakness in the parliamentary process can be overcome by plebiscites on the sorts of alternative future society might want.

Public Relations Committees
The increasing inter-relationship between science and society makes it essential for scientific societies to set up public relations committees, both for communication of information and for better understanding. Scientists often still believe that their devotion to pure science is in some way contaminated by involvement in issues of public interest. They will need to change.

Science-oriented Civil Liberties Committees
A number of civil liberties associations flourish in most democratic countries, but it is only incidentally, if at all, that they consider science issues. We need to have civil liberties organizations which are specially concerned with the impact of science on civil liberties.

Scientific Journalism

Science reporting, if taken more seriously, will become increasingly important. It will become a regular item of news coverage like foreign news, and special journalists will be trained for it.

Citizens' Committees

Citizens' committees have constantly demonstrated their value in stopping or modifying socially harmful technology. Such committees have been hampered in the past, however, by a lack of recognition, information and funds.

Traditional legal rules have required that a party to an action have a direct interest in its subject matter. To prevent pollution from a river, for example, I must show that my paddock is irrigated by it and that I have suffered property damage. We need law reform which entitles a person to bring an action to protect an amenity in which he or she has no proprietary interest, such as, for example, a wildlife preserve or the beach. An extension of this principle will enable concerned groups to litigate to preserve the rights of posterity. At present, such groups are denied any sort of legal hearing.

Citizens' committees also need more information as a matter of right from governments and corporations, for which the law must provide through freedom of information acts. They also need guidance on the intricacies of piloting a case through the rules and regulations of statutory bodies. Ralph Nader's *Action for Change: A Student Manual of Public Interest Organising* is a step in this direction. Other jurisdictions need similar guidelines.

Closing the Communications Gap

Interesting studies have been conducted on the communication gap between law and science. One such, conducted by the Oak Ridge National Laboratory in the United States under the sponsorship of the National Science Foundation, sent out a circular to 2,300 lawyers working in the area of natural resources and environmental management law, of whom 575 responded.[15]

Although there was a tendency to fix less blame on lawyers, several respondents felt that the blame must be shared equally between the two disciplines. Some saw both professions as using too much jargon: lawyers writing for lawyers and scientists for scientists.

Some features of the scientific attitude and method which attracted criticism were the peer approval systems of science, the failure of scientists to be sufficiently vocal in public debate, and the publication and distribution policies of scientific literature.

Committees of Inquiry into Technological Change

The Myers Committee, which was appointed to inquire into the economic and social effect of technological change in Australia, published its report in 1980, and drew attention to the difficulties involved in the process of adjustment to technological change and to the necessity for the 'social partners' – government, unions and employers – to consult each other. Employment opportunities could also be anticipated and prepared for in this way.

A Commission on the Integrity of the Human Body

Whether and to what extent the human body can be tampered with are policy decisions for the community, and indeed for the international community, and are too serious to be left to scientists. Before the turn of the century, dramatic new developments will make far deeper inroads on bodily integrity.

A commission which reports on the areas of threat to bodily integrity could stimulate a more timely legislative response. According to some forecasts, developments such as cloning, pre-selection of sex, and full-term test-tube babies are possibilities by the turn of the century. An annual report by a commission outlining the occurrences of the previous year and the dangers which are imminent will remove much of the haziness of any public debate. This is a function that an agency of the UN, such as the World Health Organization, could best perform. Such reports should be required by statute to be tabled in every national legislature.

Centres for Studying Legal Restraints on Weapons Science

There has been comparatively little research into the violations of basic legal rights by the arms trade. The smokescreen of defence and military emergencies inhibits lawyers from undertaking such enquiries despite the peacetime conditions in which the armaments industry conducts most of its operations. There is little doubt, however, that many civil liberties and human rights rules and principles can be invoked nationally and internationally to restrain some aspects of this activity. Study centres promoting such research are vital. Without any legal requirements of disclosure of information, peace-loving people are persuaded to invest their life-savings in companies specializing in the manufacture of weapons of death. The scientific resources of universities are extensively used for these lethal purposes. More than half the world's scientific manpower and more than a thousand million dollars a day are funnelled into our most inhuman activity without any hindrance from the law.

Data Protection Authorities

The possible abuses of computerized information need far more surveillance than current legal structures afford. The infringements of privacy and of basic rights – even the right to employment – resulting from the abuse of data are so numerous that they require a special authority to oversee them. The courts are too busy and too formal for this purpose. Penal powers are not essential, for such a body can function very much along the lines of a press council, contenting itself with investigation and giving maximum publicity to its findings.

The same organization could be used to deal with computer crime. The police force often lacks the expertise to handle the very sophisticated investigations required, and data protection committees could be a valuable reservoir of expertise upon which the police could draw.

Privacy Protection Authorities

Privacy protection authorities would perform the functions in the area of privacy that data protection committees could perform in the computer field. They would concern themselves with the investigation and control of surveillance of all sorts. The easy availability of surveillance devices will let the situation get out of control unless some authority keeps a continuous watch on it. Privacy committees are overdue in the common law jurisdictions and New South Wales was one of the pioneers in setting up such a committee.

The powers of the authority, like the powers of the data protection committee, or of the press council, could be investigatory rather than punitive. Indeed, in the case of all these authorities, it is important that they do not constitute encroachments upon the authority of the ordinary courts.

Cybernetic Survey Commissions

With the progress of cybernetic science (the study of systems of control through electronic devices) the frontiers of machine decision making will push back the frontiers of human decision making. There will be a natural tendency for the computer to be used for decisions involving even a humanistic element as, for example, in the imposition of routine fines or the determination of alimony in a matrimonial action. The progressive increase of such uses needs to be monitored.

There is also a fear that when a machine is invented which will teach itself, it will be a danger to us. We do not know when this machine will appear, but already supercomputers, such as the newly released Cray-2, are reported to be several hundred times faster than the largest IBM machines currently available.[16]

Cybernetic survey commissions would have jurisdiction to call for information on developments in this field, to study their implications on basic rights, and to publicize the information. Such a commission would be society's insurance against the possibility of mankind abdicating some basic and essential powers to machines.

Waste-Watch Organs

Modern society lacks bodies specially charged with the duty of noting and controlling areas in which modern technology wastefully uses scarce natural resources.[17] Waste will be one of the great political issues of the future and one of posterity's principal grievances against the present. Our age, increasingly conscious of its duties towards posterity, is ill equipped governmentally if it does not institutionalize its waste-watch operations.

Waste watch will mean more controls. A rigidly administered permit system may determine when and by whom materials are to be used. But controls engender bureaucracy and bureaucratic excesses. How these are to be prevented are matters for attention now.

Waste watch will also involve research, for many engineering undertakings, for example, make wasteful use of material. Similarly, miniaturization, a great material-saving idea of the future, will need to be more amply researched. The US engineer, Buckminster Fuller, has given brilliant leadership in this area, showing how a minimum of materials can be used to produce a maximum of results.

Independent Authorities for Product Recall

Technology and industry often combine to produce goods that are basically dangerous or unfit for the purpose for which they were bought. Proof that these goods are unfit or dangerous may depend on technology which is often in the exclusive command of the manufacturer. Pesticides, paints and industrial chemicals, for example, often continue to be used despite the damage they cause to health and life. Ralph Nader has shown how some motor companies have failed, for reasons of cost, to build in specified safety features in their cars.[18] An independent authority could be vested with the power to recall these products.

Restructuring Education Syllabuses

When students are introduced to science in schools there is invariably no presentation of its social implications.

Science should be taught in such a way that it demonstrates the social problems posed by modern technology.

In addition, the sociology of science should be a compulsory component of every science course offered at tertiary level.

Law School Curricula
Law school curricula could be refashioned to equip lawyers with skills to deal with the demands of the scientific age.

Law schools could offer a variety of subjects dealing with the interrelationship of science and law, one of which should be compulsory.

A course in basic scientific literacy, which would equip the student with knowledge of basic chemistry, physics, and biology could be offered.

A course on science and social responsibility could be added to existing jurisprudence courses, especially those already based on sociology.

Research programmes which law students undertake at law school could include at least one piece of research and writing in the area of law, science and technology.

Law faculties could build up contacts with institutions which examine and disseminate scientific knowledge. The Scientists' Institute for Public Information was founded for this purpose in the US in 1963. Australia has the Scientific Policy Studies Section of the Department of Science and the Environment in the national capital.

Current courses in constitutional law, government and politics seem heavily anchored to the past. They will need to develop futuristic perspectives which will be of growing importance in all studies of law and government.

Interdisciplinary Education
Interdisciplinary courses should be offered in tertiary education to provide staff for technology assessment for future civil liberties movements, and for training future bureaucrats.

At Boston University Law School's Center for Law and Health Sciences law students meet and work with graduate students from other disciplines, earning academic credits for this work. In a summer pilot programme, fifteen graduate students from Boston, Brandeis, Harvard and the Massachusetts Institute of Technology were divided into four interdisciplinary teams each of which worked on a complex problem, such as genetic counselling. Monash University's graduate school of environmental science is an outstanding Australian example of interdisciplinary education and team work.

Courses in Technology Assessment and Futurology
Although all the consequences of a decision cannot possibly be foreseen, we are certainly now in a position to see a few further steps ahead than was possible earlier. Trained futurists, aided by computer models, are now in a position to see the possible consequences of a decision well ahead.

Courses in technology assessment and futurology were beginning to be offered at US universities in the early 1970s, starting with a course in the University of Maryland's Chemical Engineering department and at Harvard University's School of Engineering. Courses on futures are also being offered in law, although there are only a few of them.

Workshops of Lawyers and Scientists
There is still a marked lack of enthusiasm on the part of lawyers and scientists for multi-disciplinary activities. Many attempts have been made. The National Conference of Lawyers and Scientists, for example, convened a workshop in Virginia in 1978 on cross-education of lawyers and scientists, including an equal number of representatives of the American Bar Association and the American Association for the Advancement of Science. The workshop considered such matters as the traditional barriers to law/science education, multi-disciplinary education in continuing education programmes, ways of encouraging education of lawyers about scientific methodology, and ways of encouraging education of scientists about legal process.[19]

Science Reporting
The public should be given more reports on science, and scientific projects. Journalistic associations could contribute

by funding courses at tertiary institutions to teach specialized scientific reporting.

One reason why scientists have been able to pursue their activities free of public scrutiny is that although 'political' politics is subjected to exposure in the press, the politics of science, though often just as political, has nearly altogether avoided scrutiny.

Institutions for the Study of Humanistic Science

In recent years, there has been an emphasis on those branches of science pertaining to life and the life sciences. An institution such as the Mitsubishi Kasei Institute of Life Sciences in Tokyo (financed by the Mitsubishi Corporation) emphasizes the humanistic aspects of science and promotes cross-disciplinary and public understanding of the inter-relationship between science and society. Other similar institutions could be set up under the aegis of governments, private enterprise, or other academic bodies.

Re-orientation of Public Attitudes

A concerted educational effort is required on the part of governments, scientific establishments, educational authorities, and public interest organizations to re-orientate public attitudes towards science. All or any of the organizations set out in this chapter can make their contribution to this effort.

Re-examination of the Learning Process

How does mankind learn the skills essential for survival in a world of unprecedented situations? Experiential learning processes, no longer adequate to meet this need, will yield to anticipatory processes. Law, experientially structured, will need anticipatory structuring. The learning process in many of its aspects will need to be overhauled. The Club of Rome has launched an important study of the learning process. Governments and other organizations must follow.

Education in the Use of Leisure

Modern science and technology have greatly reduced the number of hours of labour needed from the average worker.

With increasing computerization, the number of leisure hours available for most people will dramatically increase. By the end of the century, many of the industrialized countries will require workers to be at their desks for only an hour or two each day. Indeed, they may not even need to attend their places of work.

A large number of people will be unprepared for their increased leisure time. United Nations' studies have shown the need to formulate educational programmes for using leisure. There is urgent work to be done in this area, especially in the industrialized countries.

Education in Ways of Living for the Future

A technological society depends on an ever-rising curve of production and its attendant waste. The elimination of waste cannot be achieved without an alteration of attitudes and ways of living. It is important, therefore, that students be shown how ways of living can be simplified without diminution and indeed with enrichment of the quality of life.

Such teaching should not involve an attempt to pressure schoolchildren into suggested alternative lifestyles but try to make them aware of the alternatives that are not based on material possessions and consumer goods. Preparing students for tomorrow requires that the teacher teach *styles* of life as much as the *facts* of life.[20]

Whither Law, Science and Society?

Some of the principles discussed in this chapter may provide the basis for a new jurisprudence for science. Some jurists have envisaged that even as mankind has lived thus far under the regime of law it may in the future be constrained to live under the rule of science.[21] If this is a possibility, new structures must evolve now.

As we move on to the close of this century and the beginning of the next, and as society's centre of gravity shifts inexorably towards technology, many areas will need to be rethought. The relative disparity which now exists between scientific and non-scientific skill will soon increase alarmingly, relegating non-scientific knowledge and skills to an ever-shrinking corner of human activity. If the law is to come to grips with science, it must do so now.

Arthur Clark, in *The Children of Icarus*, has observed that we are now in a phase when 'history is holding its breath and the present is detaching itself from the past like an iceberg that has broken away from its icy moorings to sail across the boundless ocean'. We need the combined wisdom of scientist, lawyer and layman lest we drift to our destruction on these uncharted seas.

References

1. Science, Law and the Citizen

1. *Age*, 29 June 1976, p. 8.
2. Swedish Peace Research Institute finding, 1978.
3. There were 604 in the first nine months of 1976 alone.
4. White Paper on Computers and Privacy, 1972.
5. For these details see *The Sunday Times*, 2 July 1978, p. 12.
6. *Age*, 1 August 1981.
7. *Age*, 14 August 1981.
8. D. H. Meadows, *et al.*, *The Limits to Growth*, Signet Books, 1972, pp. 92-3.

2. Human Rights, Law and Technology

1. See Lord Radcliffe, *The Law and its Compass*, Northwestern University Press, 1960.
2. G. Dunea, 'Hyperactive Judges', *British Medical Journal*, vol. 281, 4 October 1980, p. 926.

3. Inadequacies of the Law

1. For example, see (1968) 43 Notre Dame Lawyer 633.
2. Peter Brett, 'Implications of Science for the Law', *McGill Law Journal*, vol. 18, 1972, p. 184.
3. See *The Times*, 24 June 1976, p. 17; and *The Sunday Times*, 27 June 1976, p. 15. The decision of the European Court is reported in *European Human Rights Reports*, vol. 2, 1979-80, p. 245.
4. On his ninetieth birthday, May 1962.
5. H. Green, 'The New Technological Era: A View from the Law', Monograph 1, Program of Policy Studies, George Washington University, 1967.
6. Chief Judge Bazelon writing in *Cornell Law Review*, vol. 62, 1977, p. 817.

7. See Laurence H. Tribe, 'Trial by Mathematics: Precision and Ritual in the Legal Process', *Harvard Law Review*, vol. 84, 1970-71, p. 1329; *People* v. *Collins* 68 Cal. 2d. 319, rejecting an attempt at trial by mathematics and warning that 'mathematics, a veritable sorcerer in our computerized society, while assisting a trier of fact in the search for truth, must not be allowed to cast a spell over him'.

8. In its fourth report, *Alcohol, Drugs and Driving*, Australian Law Reform Commission, p. 1.

9. *Age*, 28 October 1982.

3. *The Human Body*

1. *The Second Genesis: The Coming Control of Life*, Prentice Hall, 1970.

2. See Jose M. R. Delgado, *Physical Control of the Mind: Toward a Psycho-civilized Society*, Harper and Row, 1970.

3. Paul K. Bridges, 'A Contemporary View of Psychosurgery' in R. N. Gaind and B. L. Hudson (eds), *Current Themes in Psychiatry*, vol. 1, Macmillan, 1978, p. 307.

4. Bridges, 'A Contemporary view of Psychosurgery', pp. 311-12.

5. G. C. Tooth and M. P. Newton, Reports on Public Health No. 104, Ministry of Health, HMSO, 1961.

6. A. Clare, 'Ethics in Psychiatry' in R. N. Gaind and B. L. Hudson (eds), *Current Themes in Psychiatry*, vol. 2, Macmillan, 1979, pp. 76-7.

7. L. G. Kiloh, 'Commentary on the Report of Inquiry into Pschosurgery' *Medical Journal of Australia*, vol. 2, 1977, pp. 296-301.

8. Bruno Bettelheim, *The Informed Heart*, Thames, 1961, Ch. 6.

9. *Age*, 23 August 1981.

10. *Age*, 3 August 1980.

11. *The Times*, 29 August 1975.

12. See J. Katz, 'Education of the Physician-Investigator' in P.A. Freund, (ed.), *Experimentation with Human Subjects*, Braziller Press, 1970.

13. Australia Public Opinion Polls (The Gallup method), 4 December 1979, Poll No. 06/6/79.

14. Erica M. Bates, *The Australian and New Zealand Journal of Sociology*, vol. 15, no. 3, 1979, p. 45.

15. See E. J. Cassell, *The Healer's Art*, Penguin Books, 1978, p. 92.

16. See A. R. Holder, *Medical Malpractice Law*, 2nd ed. John Wiley, 1978, p. 17.

17. 'The Pope Speaks: The Prolongation of Life', an address to the International Congress of Anesthesiologists, 24 November 1957, *Osservatore Romano*.

18. Australian Law Reform Commission: Human Tissue Transplants (ALRC 7) 1977, 111.

19. *The Times*, 14 November 1980, p. 4.

20. *New York Times*, 21 May 1971.

21. *The Times*, 16 March 1974.

22. For these and other references from actual experience, see Frank Galbally, 'Death by Statute', *Australian Law Journal*, vol. 55, 1981, p. 339.

23. *Scientific Research and the Law*, Papers of the Tenth Council of Europe Colloquy on European Law, 23 September 1980.

24. L. Gordis and E. Gold, 'Privacy, Confidentiality and the Use of Medical Records in Research', *Science*, vol. 207, no. 4427, 11 January, 1980, p. 153.

25. See the *Australian*, 13 January 1981.

26. 'Organ Transplantation – The Legal Issues', *University of Queensland Law Journal*, vol. 6, no. 2, 1969, p. 10.

27. The Australian Law Reform Commission, Working Paper no. 5 of 1977 referring to a paper received by it from Dr Kevin Lafferty of the John Curtin School of Medical Research of the ACT.

28. T. M. S. Chang and S. K. Lo, 'Urea Removal of Urease and Ammonia Absorbents in the Intestine', *The Physiologist*, vol. 13, 1970, p. 165.

29. Carl-Goran Heden, 'Perspectives on the Medical Impact of Enzyme Engineering', Eighth CIOMS Round Table Conference, WHO, 1974, p. 279.

30. See T. M. Hartman, 'The Buying and Selling of Human Organs from the Living: Why Not?' *Akron Law Review*, vol. 13, 1979-80, p. 152. See also Russell Scott, *The Body as Property*, Allen Lane, 1981.

31. *Age*, 4 May 1981, p. 11.

32. *Age*, 25 April 1981.

33. See reports on Sydney research in this field in the *Australian*, 15 December 1976.

34. Elizabeth K. Turner, 'Thalassaemias in Australia', *Australian Family Physician*, vol. 8, 1979, pp. 409-21.

35. L. Kerr, 'New Advances in Medical Genetics', paper presented

at the 1980 ANZAAS Symposium on Human Genetics and the Law.

36. *Editorial, Medical Legal Journal*, vol. 40, 1972, p. 75.

37. *Stanford Law Review*, vol. 26, 1974, p. 1191.

38. B. J. Culliton, 'Fetal Research: The Case History of a Massachusetts Law', *Science*, vol. 187, no. 4173, 24 January 1975, p. 237.

39. Federal Register 30648 (1974).

40. *Age*, 28 January 1981.

41. *People* v. *Sorenson*, 68 Cal. 2d 280, 289, 437, 66 Cal. Rptr. 7, 13.

42. *Orford* v. *Orford, Dominion Law Reports*, vol. 58, 1921, p. 258.

43. California Civil Code, s. 216 (West Supp. 1973).

44. See *Faith and Culture*, vol. 1, Catholic Institute of Sydney, 1978, pp. 86, 95.

45. *Eisenstadt* v. *Baird* (1972) 405 US 438 at 453.

46. *Age* in reply to Professor Carl Wood's letter of 18 April 1981.

47. Professor Carl Wood, *Age*, 3 May 1981.

48. *Auckland Star*, 22 December 1980.

49. For tort, see W. L. Prosser, *Handbook of the Law of Torts*, 3rd ed., St Paul, West, 1964, p. 355: '. . . the unborn child in the path of an automobile is as much a person in the street as the mother'.

50. Alvin Toffler, *Future Shock*, Pan Books, 1970, pp. 212-4.

51. *Sun*, 3 March 1980.

52. *Age*, 9 September 1981.

53. See J. P. Fitzgerald, 'The Patentability of Living Organisms Under 35 USC s. 101: *Parker* v. *Chakrabarty*', *New England Law Review*, vol. 15, 1980, p. 379 for a full discussion of the principal issues.

54. [1972] VR 353.

55. 41 Ill. App. 2d 240, 190 NE 2d 849 (1963) cert. denied 379 US 945 (1964).

56. *Curlender* v. *Bio-Science Laboratories*, 106 Cal App. 3d 811 (1980).

57. [1933] 4 DLR 339, 345.

58. *Berman* v. *Allan* 80 NJ 421, 404 A.2d 8 (1979).

59. *Ziemba* v. *Sternberg* 357 NYS 2d 265 (1974).

60. M. Lappé, 'Ethics of In Vitro Fertilisation: Risk-Taking for the Unborn', *Hastings Center Report*, vol. 2, 1972: HR 7724, 93rd. Congress, 2d. Sess. (1974).

61. See Susan R. Izenstark, 'Genetic Manipulation: Research Regulation and Legal Liability Under International Law', *California Western International Law Journal*, vol. 7, 1977, p. 203.

62. *Poe* v. *Ullman*, 367 US 497, 552 (1961) Harlan J. dissenting, cited with approval in *Griswold* v. *Connecticut* 381 US 479 (1965).

63. Justice Goldberg in *Griswold* v. *Connecticut* 381 US 479 (1965).

64. Charles P. Kindregan, 'State Power over Human Fertility and Individual Liberty' *Hastings Law Journal*, vol. 23, 1972, pp. 1425-6.

65. Macmillan, 1971. Zhores Medvedev was head of the Department of Molecular Radiobiology at the Institute of Medical Radiology at Obninsk until his dismissal in 1969. Roy Medvedev, a scholar and historian, was dismissed in 1971 from his position as Senior Scientist at the Institute of Professional Education in Moscow.

66. Hearings on S. 974, S. 878, and S.J. Res. 71, before the Subcommittee on Health of the Senate Committee on Labor, and Public Welfare (Quality of Health Care – Human Experimentation, 1973) 93rd Congress, 1st Sess. pt 1, at 844 (1973).

67. See Hearings on Federal Involvement in the Use of Behaviour Modification Drugs on Grammar School Children before a Subcommittee of the House Committee on Government Operation (The Right to Privacy Inquiry, 1970) 91st Congress 2d Sess. 1-74 (1970).

68. See 'Notes on Anthropotelemetry: Dr Schwitzgebel's Machine', *Harvard Law Review*, vol. 80, 1966-67, p. 403.

69. R. Briggs and T. J. King, 'Transplantation of Living Nuclei from Blastula Cells into Enucleated Frogs' Eggs', *Proceedings of the National Academy of Sciences of the USA*, vol. 38, 1952, p. 455.

70. J. Lederberg, 'Experimental Genetics and Human Evolution', *American Naturalist*, vol. 100, no. 915, 1966, p. 527; P. D. Turner, 'Love's Labor Lost: Legal and Ethical Implications in Artificial Human Procreation', *University of Detroit Journal of Urban Law*, vol. 58, 1981, p. 459; *Reform*, no. 26, 1982, p. 68.

71. See Joseph Fletcher, 'Ethical Aspects of Genetic Controls', *New England Journal of Medicine*, vol. 14, 1971, p. 779, mentioning such disappearing racial types as the hairy Ainu of Japan and certain strains of the Romani gypsies.

72. *Australian*, 30 December 1980.

73. Professor Carl Wood, leader of the in-vitro fertilization team at the Queen Victoria Hospital in Melbourne, as reported in the *West Australian*, 25 September 1980, in an address to the Melbourne Rotary Club.

4. Human Society

1. Karl Bednarik, *The Programmers, Elite of Automation*, Macdonald, 1967.

2. N. Wiener, *The Human Use of Human Beings*, Eyre & Spottiswoode, 1950 p. 214.

3. Encyclopaedia Britannica, 15th ed. 1974 Macropaedia, vol. 18, 23a.

4. *New Scientist*, 13 January 1977, p. 86.

5. See 'Looking for a Data Haven', *Insight*, June 1978, p. 53.

6. For an account of this episode see Gerald McKnight, *Computer Crime*, Michael Joseph, 1973, pp. 83-90.

7. *Age*, 8 June 1981.

8. A. H. Robertson (ed.), *Privacy and Human Rights*, Manchester, 1970, p. 149.

9. See Report of the Secretary General to the Commission on Human Rights E/CN4/1116 of 23 January 1973, especially para. 89. See also the report of the Younger Committee on Privacy in the UK, reporting on the technical surveillance devices available in England, HMSO Cmd 5012, July 1972.

10. Robertson, *Privacy and Human Rights*, p. 142.

11. *Law and Computer Technology*, March/April 1972, p. 44.

12. *Anderson v. Sills* 106 NJ Super. 245, 256 A.2d. 298 (1969).

13. *Weekend Australian*, 10-11 January, 1981, p. 18.

14. Amnesty International Report on Torture, 1973, p. 43; T. Shallice, 'The Use of Sensory Deprivation in Depth Interrogation', Oslo Conference on the Abolition of Torture, 6-7 October 1973, p. 13.

15. *New Scientist*, 5 August 1976, p. 272.

16. Julius Stone, *Social Dimensions of Law and Justice*, Maitland, 1966, p. 162.

17. Robert MacNeil, *The People Machine: The Influence of Television Upon American Politics*, Eyre & Spottiswoode, 1970, p. 132.

18. Denys Thompson (ed.), *Discrimination and Popular Culture*, 2nd ed. Penguin Books, 1973, p. 71.

19. Frank George (ed.), *Science Fact*, Topaz Books, 1977, p. 154.

20. News report from Los Angeles carried in the *Age*, Melbourne, 11 March 1977.

21. Brian Martin, *The Ecologist*, vol. 11, no. 1, 1981, p. 33.

22. Hans Morgenthau, 'Modern Science and Political Power', *Columbia Law Review*, vol. 64, 1964, p. 1404.

23. Hugh Stevenson, 'The Coming Clash – The Impact of Multi-national Corporations on National States', *Saturday Review Press*, 1952; Anthony Sampson, *The Sovereign State: The Secret History of ITT*, Coronet Books, Hodder Fawcett Ltd, 1974.

24. *Age*, 26 November 1982, p. 11.

25. *New York Times*, 30 July 1978.

26. Daniel Z. Goodwill, 'A Look at the Future Impact of Computer-Communications on Everyday life', *Technological Forecasting and Social Change*, vol. 4, 1972-73, p. 228.

6. *The Human Habitat*

1. A. J. Marshall (ed.), *The Great Extermination*, Heinemann, 1966, p. 59.

2. R. and V. Routley, *The Fight for the Forests: The Takeover of Australian Forests for Pines, Woodchips and Intensive Forestry*, ANU Press, 1973, pp. 114-15.

3. W. E. Small, *Third Pollution*, Praeger, 1970, p. 14.

4. See Charles Birch, *Confronting the Future*, Penguin Books, 1975, p. 276.

5. US Council on Environmental Quality, 1972, Environmental Quality, 1972, p. 6.

6. Birch, *Confronting the Future*, p. 213.

7. *Tito and Others v. Waddell and Others (No. 2)* (1977) 2 *Weekly Law Reports* p. 496.

8. See E. H. Rabin and M. D. Schwartz (eds), *The Pollution Crisis, Official Documents*, Oceana, 1975, vol. 2, pp. 482, 509.

9. A. Nelson-Smith, *Oil Pollution and Marine Ecology*, Plenum Press, 1973, p. 103.

10. Milos Holy, *Erosion and Environment*, Pergamon Press, 1980, p. 3.

11. Birch, *Confronting the Future*, p. 109.

12. R. G. Nash and E. A. Woolson, 'Persistence of Chlorinated Hydrocarbon Insecticides in Soils', *Science*, vol. 157, no. 3791, 25 August 1967, p. 924.

13. See Amory B. Lovins, *Soft Energy Paths*, Penguin Books, 1977.

14. 1982 Yearbook of Science and the Future, Encyclopaedia Britannica, p. 222.

15. 1981 Yearbook of Science and the Future, Encyclopaedia Britannica, p. 274.

16. The proceedings of the World Climate Conference, Geneva, 1979, WMO No. 537; Encyclopaedia Britannica, 15th ed., vol. 14, 1973-74, p. 756.

17. J. Calvin Giddings, *Chemistry, Man, and Environmental Change*, Canfield Press, 1973, p. 208.

18. A. B. Pittock *et al.*, 'Human Impact on the Global Atmosphere: Implications for Australia', *Search*, vol. 12, no. 8, August 1981, p. 261.

19. *Scientific American*, August 1981, p. 115; see also the September 1981 issue of the *Scientific American* specially devoted to industrial microbiology.

20. *Omni*, September 1981, p. 20.

21. E. H. Rabin and M. D. Schwartz (eds), *The Pollution Crisis*, vol. 2, 1976, p. 423.

22. *Age*, 27 August 1981.

23. J. Paul Lomio, 'International Law and Dumping of Radioactive Wastes at Sea', *New England Law Review*, vol. 15, 1980, p. 257.

24. D. Cushing, *Marine Ecology and Fisheries*, 1975, p. 100, cited by Lomio, 'International Law and Dumping of Radioactive Wastes at Sea', p. 259.

25. *Time*, 10 October 1977, p. 27.

26. See Terence Bendixson, *Instead of Cars*, Temple Smith, 1974, p. 29. For statistical tables of the occupancy of cars, see p. 220. In the US, for example, in 1971, 34.1 per cent of travel was with an average number of 1.4 riders. Only 2.5 per cent of travel was with more than three riders. In France, the driver was alone on all but six out of every hundred trips.

27. Joe Mala *et al.*, *Solar Australia: Australia at the Crossroads*, Ambassador Press, 1977.

28. But Australia spends $750,000 on solar energy research compared with $20 million on nuclear research.

29. Susan George, *How the Other Half Dies*, Penguin Books, 1976.

30. *National Geographic Magazine*, Energy Report, 1981, p. 90.

31. See C. G. Weeramantry, *Equality and Freedom: Some Third World Perspectives*, Hansa Publishers, 1976, p. 159.

32. Birch, .*Confronting the Future*, p. 130.

33. *New York Times, Weekly Review*, 6 March 1977, p. 5.

34. Colin Norman, 'Weapons Builders Eye Civilian Reactor Fuel', *Science*, vol. 214, no. 4518, October 1981, p. 307.

35. On the legality of nuclear weapons, see the following works:

Nagendra Singh, *Nuclear Weapons and International Law*, Praegar, 1959; M. S. McDougal and F. P. Feliciano, *Law and Minimum World Public Order: The Legal Regulation of International Coercion*, Yale University Press, 1961; George Schwarzenberger, *The Legality of Nuclear Weapons*, Stevens & Sons, 1958; William B. O'Brien, *War and/or Survival*, Doubleday, 1969.

36. The author is indebted for much of the information in this section to vol. IX, no. 10, 1980 of the *Defense Monitor*, p. 5.

37. *Age*, 24 July 1979, quoting a Washington report.

38. *Defense Monitor*, vol. IX, no. 10, 1980, pp. 1 and 3.

39. Richard Falk, *A Study of Future Worlds*, The Free Press, 1975, p. 92.

40. H. Nash (ed.), *Progress as if Survival Mattered: A Handbook for a Conserver Society*, Friends of the Earth, 1977, p. 293.

41. Christopher B. Stone, 'Should Trees Have Standing? Towards Legal Rights for Natural Objects', *Southern California Law Review*, vol. 45, 1972, p. 450.

42. K. C. Davis, 'The Liberalised Law of Standing', *University of Chicago Law Review*, vol. 37, 1970, pp. 470-1; Joseph F. Di Mento, 'Citizen Environmental Legislation in the States: An Overview', *Journal of Urban Law*, vol. 53, 1976, pp. 433-5.

43. On the Stockholm Conference, see generally Louis B. Sohn, 'The Stockholm Declaration on the Human Environment', *Harvard International Law Journal*, vol. 14, 1973, p. 423.

6. Humanness and Human Dignity

1. It is to be remembered however that *homo sapiens* is itself a term of notoriously imprecise definition. Thus a comparatively recent provisional definition reads, 'A species of the genus *Homo* characterized by a mean cranial capacity of about 1,350 cc; muscular ridges on the cranium strongly marked ... (about 20 further descriptive lines) ... appendicular skeleton adapted for a fully upright posture and gait, limb bones relatively slender and straight.' W. E. Le Gros Clark, *The Fossil Evidence for Human Evolution*, University of Chicago Press, 1955.

2. For all these details and more, see the medical references in R. A. Destro, 'Research on the Fetus', *Villanova Law Review*, vol. 22, 1976-77, pp. 343-7.

3. Epistles 121.4: 'seeds are gradually formed in the uterus, and it

is not reputed homicide until the scattered elements receive their appearance and members'. Cited in J. T. Noonan (ed.), *The Morality of Abortion*, Harvard University Press, 1971, p. 15.

4. *Questions on the Heptateuch*, 80.

5. 8 *Libros Politicorum* 7:11.

6. See Noonan (ed.), *The Morality of Abortion*, p. 38, citing Zacchia's *Medico-Legal Questions*, 9:1. Zacchia is described as the 'General Proto-Physician of the Whole Roman Ecclesiastical State'.

7. Under the Bull *Apostolicae Sedis*.

8. See also the new Code of Canon Law, 1917 which draws no distinction between various stages of formation of the foetus.

9. *Allocution to Midwives*, 29 October 1951, cited by D. Granfield, *The Abortion Decision*, Doubleday, 1969, p. 69.

10. W. M. Abbott (ed.), *Documents of Vatican II*, Geoffrey Chapman, 1966, p. 203.

11. See generally, Noonan, *The Morality of Abortion*.

12. Y. K. Miklishanski, 'The Law of the Foetus', *Jubilee Volume in Honour of Simon Federbush*, Mosad Harav Kook, 1961, pp. 251-60.

13. M. Maimonides, *Laws of Homicide*, 2.6. See also Exodus 21:22 excluding a non-viable child from the category of 'man'.

14. Coke, *Institutes of the Laws of England*, iii, 3.7

15. 7 Will 4 and 1 Vict. c. 85, 1837.

16. *Sentence of Death (Expectant Mothers) Act*, 1931

17. *Infant Life (Preservation) Act* 1929, s.1(i).

18. *R. v. Bourne* [1939] 1 K B 687; (1938) 3 All E R 615.

19. S.2; ss. 1(a) and 1(b).

20. [1969] VR 667.

21. (1971) 3 DCR NSW 25 at 29.

22. *Amendment to Criminal Law (Consolidation) Act*, 1969; s.82A.

23. 410 US 113 (1943) esp. at 162.

24. *World Medical Association Bulletin*, vol. 2, 1950, pp. 5-34. See also the Declaration of Oslo, which enjoins 'the utmost respect for human life from the time of conception.'

25. See the translation of this German decision in J. D. Gorby and R. E. Jones, 'West German Abortion Decision: A Contrast to *Roe v. Wade*', *John Marshall Journal of Practice and Procedure*, vol. 9, 1976, p. 641.

26. M. Revillard, 'Legal Aspects of Artificial Insemination and Embryo Transfer in French Law', *International and Comparative Law Quarterly*, vol. 23, 1974, p. 383.

27. Dennis J. Horan, *Villanova Law Review*, vol. 22, 1976-77, p. 338.

28. Vatican II: The Church in the Modern World, s.2-87.

29. See, for example, R. A. McCormick, 'Notes on Moral Theology', *Theological Studies*, vol. 30, 1969, p. 680: all asexual reproduction condemned; Paul Ramsey, 'Moral and Religious Implications of Genetic Control' in J. D. Rosltansky (ed.), *Genetics and the Future of Man*, North-Holland 1966, pp. 107-69: reproduction must be done heterosexually by human intercourse within the context of marriage and the family, see also Philip Edgcumbe Hughes, 'Theological Principles in the Control of Human Life', in W. Spitzer and C. Saylor (eds), *Birth Control and the Christian: A Protestant Symposium on the Control of Human Reproduction*, Tyndale House, 1969, p. 146.

30. For references, see C. P. Kindregan, *Hastings Law Journal*, vol. 23, 1972, p. 1423.

31. P. Teilhard de Chardin, *The Phenomenon of Man*, B. Wall (trans.), Collins, 1959, p. 282.

32. 'Ethical Aspects of Genetic Controls', *New England Journal of Medicine*, vol. 285, no. 14, 1971, p. 776.

33. R. Scott, *The Body as Property*, Allen Lane, 1981, pp. 199-200.

34. *Time*, 31 July 1978, p. 68.

35. Julius Stone, 'Knowledge, Survival and the Duties of Science' *American University Law Review*, vol. 23, 1973, p. 231.

36. See B. F. Skinner, *Beyond Freedom and Dignity*, Penguin Books, 1974, pp. 31-62.

37. In his dissent in (1928) 277 US 438 at 473-4.

38. For example, for Australia, see the reference to this lacuna in *Victoria Park Racing and Recreation Grounds Co. Ltd v. Taylor* (1937) 58 CLR 479.

8. Power, Ethics, and Responsibility

1. See Will Durant, *The Story of Philosophy*, Time Inc., 1926, p. 129.

2. *The New Atlantis*, Cambridge University Press, 1900, p. 34.

3. H. Rose and S. Rose, *Science and Society*, Penguin Books, 1969, p. 33. The authors point out, on the basis of a 1961 London University research thesis by M. Pike, that when the income necessary to maintain a middle-class life was £200–£1,000 per annum, a chemist's starting salary was $25 per annum.

4. OECD Report, *Science, Growth and Society*, 1971, pp. 30-52, 90-91.

5. Aldous Huxley, *Brave New World*, The Vanguard Library, 1952.

6. Oswald Spengler, *The Decline of the West*, George Allen & Unwin, 1932.

7. Lewis Mumford, *The Myth of the Machine*, Secker and Warburg, 1967; *The Pentagon of Power*, Secker and Warburg, 1971.

8. The manifesto jointly issued in July 1955, by Albert Einstein and Bertrand Russell, known as the Einstein-Russell manifesto.

9. Arthur Koestler, *The Sleepwalkers*, Penguin Books, 1964.

10. Charles Reich, *The Greening of America*, Penguin Books, 1974.

11. Daniel S. Greenberg, *The Politics of American Science*, Penguin Books, 1969.

12. Ralph Nader (ed.), *The Consumer and Corporate Accountability*, Harcourt Brace Jovanovich, 1973.

13. Theodore Roszak, *The Making of a Counter Culture: Reflections on the Technocratic Society and its Youthful Opposition*, Faber & Faber, 1971, xiii.

14. J. D. Bernal, *Marx and Science*, Lawrence & Wishart, 1952; *The Social Function of Science*, MIT Press, 1967; Michael Polanyi, 'The Republic of Science', *Minerva*, vol. 1 (Autumn), 1962, p. 54; 'The Growth of Science in Society', *Minerva*, vol. 4 (Summer), 1967, p. 533.

15. R. K. Merton, 'Science and Technology in a Democratic Order', *Journal of Legal and Political Science*, vol. 1, 1942, pp. 115-26.

16. R. W. Reid, *Tongues of Conscience*, Constable, 1969, pp. 103, 214.

17. Hans Morgenthau, 'Modern Science and Political Power', *Columbia Law Review*, vol. 64, 1964, p. 1404.

18. Barry Commoner, *Science and Survival*, Ballantine Books, 1963, pp. 61-2, citing C. E. McIlwain, 'The Radiation Belts, Natural and Artificial', *Science*, vol. 142, 18 October 1963, p. 355.

19. B. Dixon, *What is Science For?* Penguin Books, 1976, pp. 110-12.

20. Nader, *The Consumer and Corporate Accountability*.

21. *Bulletin*, 17 September 1977, pp. 38-9.

22. See Greenberg, *The Politics of American Science*.

23. So named after the Mohorovic depression in the earth's crust, where the 'hole' was to be made.

24. See Greenberg, *The Politics of American Science*, pp. 222-3.

25. William H. Whyte, *The Organisation Man*, Penguin Books, 1976, p. 201.
26. Whyte, *The Organisation Man*, p. 203.

9. Academic Freedom and the Law

1. Julius Stone, 'Knowledge, Survival and the Duties of Science', *American Universities Law Review*, vol. 23, 1973, p. 259.

2. *Donoghue* v. *Stevenson* [1932] AC 562.

3. *Rylands* v. *Fletcher* [1866] LR 1 Ex 265; (1868) LR 3 HL 330.

10. Inadequate Political Structures

1. Charles Reich, *The Greening of America*, Random House, 1970, p. 90.

2. Herbert Marcuse, *One-Dimensional Man: The Ideology of Industrial Society*, Sphere Books, 1968. See also Ralph Miliband, *The State in Capitalist Society*, Weidenfeld and Nicolson, 1969, p. 237.

3. See Lewis Mumford, *The Pentagon of Power*, Secker and Warburg, 1971; *The Myth of the Machine*, Secker and Warburg, 1967.

4. E. F. Schumacher, *Small is Beautiful*, Abacus, Sphere Books, 1974. See also Theodore Roszack, *The Making of Counter Culture: Reflections on the Technocratic Society and its Youthful Opposition*, Faber & Faber, 1970, pp. 266-7.

5. .Vance Packard, *The Waste Makers*, David McKay & Co. 1960.

6. Robert Heilbroner, *The Future as History*, Harper Torchbooks, 1968, p. 167.

7. N. Rotenstreich, 'Technology and Politics', *International Philosophical Quarterly*, vol. vii, 1967, p. 197.

8. Victor C. Ferkiss, *Technological Man*, Heinemann 1969, pp. 181-2.

9. R. Buckminster Fuller, *Utopia or Oblivion*, Penguin Books, 1970.

10. Daniel Bell, 'The Post-Industrial Society: A Speculative View' in E. and E. Hutchings (eds), *Scientific Progress and Human Values*, American Elsevoir, 1967, p. 157.

11. Hutchings (ed.), *Scientific Progress and Human Values*, p.168.

12. Z. Brzezinski, 'America in the Technetronic Age', *Encounter*, vol. 30, 1968, p. 16.

13. J. Harvey Wheeler, *Democracy in a Revolutionary Era: The Political Order Today*, Praeger, 1968.

14. Roger Williams, *Politics and Technology*, Macmillan, 1971, p. 47. This is one of the best short summaries of the learning on this subject.

15. See *Time*, 7 August 1958, 'Lobbyists: Do They Run America?'

16. Michael Polanyi, 'The Nature of Scientific Convictions', *The Nineteenth Century*, July 1949, p. 14.

17. Some futurists feel that the need to anticipate change is so great as to necessitate the introduction in school curricula of the subject 'Futures', to be taught as a department of study comparable to History: see Toffler's interview in the *Age*, 7 December 1972.

18. Mumford, *The Pentagon of Power*, p. 410.

19. Cf. The National Goals Research Staff appointed by President Nixon or the high powered commission appointed by President Eisenhower, which produced its report, *National Goals for Americans*, Prentice-Hall, 1960.

11. Agenda for Action

1. See Michael S. Baram, 'Technology Assessment and Social Control', *Science*, vol. 180, 4 May 1973, p. 470.

2. For a full survey of technology assessment, see 'Readings in Technology Assessment', August 1975, a compendious collection of papers issued by the Program of Policy Studies in Science and Technology, George Washington University, Washington D.C.

3. See for suggestions, Alvin Toffler, 'What is Anticipatory?', *Futurist*, vol. IX, 1975, p. 224.

4. A series of United States cases involving the conflict between the teaching of the Biblical account of creation and the evolutionary theory were resolved in favour of science in the United States. These could be answered differently in other jurisdictions. For references to the United States cases, see S. Goldberg, *The University of Illinois Law Forum*, vol. 1, 1979, p. 1.

5. See A. Toffler, *Future Shock*, Pan Books, 1970, p. 348.

6. On the various roles that lawyers can play in technology assessment, see Joseph C. Goulden, *The Superlawyers*, Weybright and Telley, p. 15, and 'The Role of Law and Lawyers in Technology Assessment' in Marvin J. Cetron and Bodo Bartocha (eds), *Technology Assessment in a Dynamic Environment*, Gordon & Breach, 1973, p. 629.

7. See G. Goyder, *The Responsible Company*, Basil Blackwell, 1961,

pp. 62*ff*; note in particular the proposals and illustrations contained in part II of this volume.

8. This suggestion was made by J. Harvey Wheeler in 'Bringing Science Under Law', *Dialogue*, vol. 4, 1971, pp. 104*ff*.

9. See J. N. Martin, 'The Science Court Proposal', *Harvard Journal on Legislation*, vol. 16, 1979, p. 443.

10. Arnold Toynbee, 'After the Age of Affluence', *The Observer*, 14 April 1974.

11. *North-South: A Programme for Survival*, Pan Books, 1980, p. 197.

12. This led to the Pugwash movement, by which Cyrus Eaton, Cleveland industrialist, financed meetings of leading scientists at Pugwash, his birthplace, and afforded a forum and means of expression for scientists in the cause of peace.

13. *Journal of the Royal Society of Arts*, April 1966. The suggested oath reads: 'On becoming a Chartered Engineer I vow to use my best endeavours to consider how my engineering skill may contribute towards the happiness of mankind.'

14. *Nature*, vol. 295, 4 February 1982, pp. 358-9.

15. *American Bar Association Journal*, vol. 59, 1973, p. 157.

16. *Newsweek*, 11 January 1982, p. 33.

17. See Vance Packard, *The Waste Makers*, David McKay Co., 1960.

18. *Unsafe at Any Speed*, Bantam Books, 1973.

19. For details regarding this workshop, see William A. Thomas, 'A Report From the Workshop on Cross-Education of Lawyers and Scientists', *Jurimetrics Journal*, vol. 19, 1978, p. 92.

20. Donald N. Michael, *The Unprepared Society: Planning for a Precarious Future*, Basic Books, 1968. This book has been criticized as largely delegating the task to the educational establishment: see *American Sociological Review*, vol. 34, 1969, p. 957. There is no gainsaying, however, that the preparation of educators is one of the important aspects needing attention. This is of course only one item on a many-point programme.

21. W. Seagle, *The Quest for Law*, Alfred A. Knopf, 1941, p. 374.

Index